Fresh Market
Caneberry Production Manual

Mark Bolda

UC Cooperative Extension Farm Advisor, Santa Cruz County

Mark Gaskell

UC Cooperative Extension Farm Advisor, Santa Barbara County

Elizabeth Mitcham

UC Cooperative Extension and AES Postharvest Pomologist
University of California, Davis

Michael Cahn

UC Cooperative Extension Farm Advisor, Monterey County

University *of* **California**
Agriculture and Natural Resources
Oakland, California
Publication 3525

To order or obtain ANR publications and other products, visit the ANR Communication Services online catalog at http://anrcatalog.ucanr.edu or phone 1-800-994-8849. You can also place orders by mail or FAX, or request a printed catalog of our products from

University of California
Agriculture and Natural Resources
Communication Services
1301 S. 46th Street
Building 478 - MC 3580
Richmond, CA 94804-4600
Telephone 1-800-994-8849 • 510-665-2195
FAX 510-665-3427
E-mail: anrcatalog.ucanr.edu

Publication 3525
ISBN-13: 978-1-60107-697-7
Illustration and photo credits given in the captions. Cover photo by Ed Show; production by Robin Walton.

Library of Congress Cataloging-in-Publication Data

Fresh market caneberry production manual / Mark Bolda ... [et al.].
    p. cm. -- (Publication ; 3525)
  Includes bibliographical references and index.
  ISBN 978-1-60107-697-7
1. Blackberries--California. 2. Raspberries--California.
3. Rubus--California. I. Bolda, Mark. II. University of California (System). Division of Agriculture and Natural Resources. III. Series: Publication (University of California (System). Division of Agriculture and Natural Resources) ; 3525.
  SB386.B6F74 2012
  634'.7109794--dc23
                        2012030148

For information about ordering this publication, telephone 1-800-994-8849.

To simplify information, trade names of products have been used. No endorsement of named or illustrated products is intended, nor is criticism implied of similar products that are not mentioned or illustrated.

UC PEER REVIEWED This publication has been anonymously peer reviewed for technical accuracy by University of California scientists and other qualified professionals. This review process was managed by ANR Associate Editor for Pomology, Viticulture, and Subtropical Horticulture, Ben Faber.

 Printed in the United States on recycled paper.

3m-pr-9/12-LR/RW

GENERAL WARNING:

WARNING ON THE USE OF CHEMICALS

Pesticides are poisonous. Always read and carefully follow all precautions and safety recommendations given on the container label. Store all chemicals in the original labeled containers in a locked cabinet or shed, away from food or feeds, and out of the reach of children, unauthorized persons, pets, and livestock.

Confine chemicals to the property being treated. Avoid drift onto neighboring properties, especially gardens containing fruits or vegetables ready to be picked.

Do not place containers containing pesticide in the trash nor pour pesticides down sink or toilet. Either use the pesticide according to the label or take unwanted pesticides to a Household Hazardous Waste Collection site. Contact your county agricultural commissioner for additional information on safe container disposal and for the location of the Hazardous Waste Collection site nearest you.

Dispose of empty containers by following label directions. Never reuse or burn the containers or dispose of them in such a manner that they may contaminate water supplies or natural waterways.

HOMEOWNER WARNING:

WARNING ON THE USE OF CHEMICALS

Pesticides are poisonous. Always read and carefully follow all precautions and safety recommendations given on the container label. Store all chemicals in their original labeled containers in a locked cabinet or shed, away from foods or feeds, and out of the reach of children, unauthorized persons, pets, and livestock.

Confine pesticides to the property being treated. Avoid drift onto neighboring properties or gardens containing fruits and/or vegetables ready to be picked.

Dispose of empty containers carefully. Follow label instructions for disposal. Never reuse the containers. Make sure empty containers are not accessible to children or animals. Never dispose of containers where they may contaminate water supplies or natural waterways. Do not pour down sink or toilet. Consult your county agricultural commissioner for correct ways of disposing of excess pesticides. Never burn pesticide containers.

PHYTOTOXICITY: Certain chemicals may cause plant injury if used at the wrong stage of plant development or when temperatures are too high. Injury may also result from excessive amounts or the wrong formulation or from mixing incompatible materials. Inert ingredients, such as wetters, spreaders, emulsifiers, diluents, and solvents, can cause plant injury. Since formulations are often changed by manufacturers, it is possible that plant injury may occur, even though no injury was noted in previous seasons.

COMMERCIAL GROWER WARNING:

WARNING ON THE USE OF CHEMICALS

Pesticides are poisonous. Always read and carefully follow all precautions and safety recommendations given on the container label. Store all chemicals in their original labeled containers in a locked cabinet or shed, away from foods or feeds, and out of the reach of children, unauthorized persons, pets, and livestock.

Recommendations are based on the best information currently available, and treatments based on them should not leave residues exceeding the tolerance established for any particular chemical. Confine chemicals to the area being treated. THE GROWER IS LEGALLY RESPONSIBLE for residues on the grower's crops as well as for problems caused by drift from the grower's property to other properties or crops.

Consult your county agricultural commissioner for correct methods of disposing of leftover spray materials and empty containers. Never burn pesticide containers.

PHYTOTOXICITY: Certain chemicals may cause plant injury if used at the wrong stage of plant development or when temperatures are too high. Injury may also result from excessive amounts or the wrong formulation or from mixing incompatible materials. Inert ingredients, such as wetters, spreaders, emulsifiers, diluents, and solvents, can cause plant injury. Since formulations are often changed by manufacturers, it is possible that plant injury may occur, even though no injury was noted in previous seasons.

IPM WARNING

PRECAUTIONS FOR USING PESTICIDES (IPM)

Pesticides are poisonous and must be used with caution. READ THE LABEL CAREFULLY BEFORE OPENING A PESTICIDE CONTAINER. Follow all label precautions and directions, including requirements for protective equipment. Use a pesticide only on crops specified on the label. Apply pesticides at the rates specified on the label or at lower rates if suggested in this publication. In California, all agricultural uses of pesticides must be reported. Contact your county agricultural commissioner for details. Laws, regulations, and information concerning pesticides change frequently, so be sure the publication you are using is up to date.

LEGAL RESPONSIBILITY. The user is legally responsible for any damage due to misuse of pesticides. Responsibility extends to effects caused by drift, runoff, or residues.

TRANSPORTATION. Do not ship or carry pesticides together with foods or feeds in a way that allows contamination of the edible items. Never transport pesticides in a closed passenger vehicle or in a closed cab.

STORAGE. Keep pesticides in original containers until used. Store them in a locked cabinet, building, or fenced area where they are not accessible to children, unauthorized persons, pets, or livestock. DO NOT store pesticides with foods, feeds, fertilizers, or other materials that may become contaminated by the pesticides.

continued on next page

IPM Warning, continued from previous page

CONTAINER DISPOSAL. Dispose of empty containers carefully. Never reuse them. Make sure empty containers are not accessible to children or animals. Never dispose of containers where they may contaminate water supplies or natural waterways. Consult your county agricultural commissioner for correct procedures for handling and disposal of large quantities of empty containers.

PROTECTION OF NONPEST ANIMALS AND PLANTS. Many pesticides are toxic to useful or desirable animals, including honey bees, natural enemies, fish, domestic animals, and birds. Crops and other plants may also be damaged by misapplied pesticides. Take precautions to protect nonpest species from direct exposure to pesticides and from contamination due to drift, runoff, or residues. Certain rodenticides may pose a special hazard to animals that eat poisoned rodents.

POSTING TREATED FIELDS. For some materials, re-entry intervals are established to protect fieldworkers. Keep workers out of the field for the required time after application and, when required by regulations, post the treated areas with signs indicating the safe re-entry date.

HARVEST INTERVALS. Some materials or rates cannot be used in certain crops within a specific time before harvest. Follow pesticide label instructions and allow the required time between application and harvest.

PERMIT REQUIREMENTS. Many pesticides require a permit from the county agricultural commissioner before possession or use. When such materials are recommended in this publication, they are marked with an asterisk (*).

PROCESSED CROPS. Some processors will not accept a crop treated with certain chemicals. If your crop is going to a processor, be sure to check with the processor before applying a pesticide.

CROP INJURY. Certain chemicals may cause injury to crops (phytotoxicity) under certain conditions. Always consult the label for limitations. Before applying any pesticide, take into account the stage of plant development, the soil type and condition, the temperature, moisture, and wind direction. Injury may also result from the use of incompatible materials.

PERSONAL SAFETY. Follow label directions carefully. Avoid splashing, spilling, leaks, spray drift, and contamination of clothing. NEVER eat, smoke, drink, or chew while using pesticides. Provide for emergency medical care IN ADVANCE as required by regulation.

PLANT WARNING:

PESTICIDE USE WARNING—READ THE LABEL

Pesticides are poisonous and must be used with caution. READ THE LABEL CAREFULLY BEFORE OPENING A CONTAINER. Precautions and directions MUST be followed exactly. Special protective equipment, as indicated on the label, must be used.

STORAGE. Keep all pesticides in original containers only. Store separately in a locked shed or area. Keep all pesticides out of the reach of children, unauthorized personnel, pets, and livestock. DO NOT STORE with foods, feeds, or fertilizers. Post warning signs on pesticide storage areas.

USE. The suggestions given in this publication are based upon best current information. Follow directions. Measure accurately to avoid residues exceeding established tolerances. Use exact amounts as indicated on the label, or use lesser amounts as suggested in this publication. Use a pesticide only on crops, plants, or animals shown on the label.

CONTAINER DISPOSAL and TRANSPORTATION. Consult your county agricultural commissioner for correct procedures for rinsing and disposing of empty containers. Do not transport pesticides in vehicles with foods, feeds, clothing, or other materials, and never in a closed cab with the vehicle driver.

RESPONSIBILITY. The grower is legally responsible for proper use of pesticides, including drift to other crops or properties, and for excessive residues. Pesticides should not be applied over streams, rivers, ponds, lakes, runoff irrigation, or other aquatic areas, except where specific use for that purpose is intended.

BENEFICIAL INSECTS. Many pesticides are highly toxic to honey bees and other beneficial insects. The farmer, the beekeeper, and the pest control industry should cooperate closely to keep losses of beneficial species to a minimum.

PROCESSED CROPS. Some processors will not accept a crop treated with certain chemicals. If your crop is going to a processor, be sure to check with the processor before making a pesticide application.

POSTING TREATED FIELDS. When worker safety re-entry intervals are established, be sure to keep workers out and post the treated areas with signs when required, indicating the safe re-entry date.

PERMIT REQUIREMENTS. Many pesticides require a permit from the County agricultural commissioner before possession or use. When such compounds are recommended in this publication, they are marked with an asterisk (*).

PLANT INJURY. Certain chemicals may cause injury or give less than optimum pest control if used at the wrong stage of plant development, in certain soil types, when temperatures are too high or too low, when the wrong formulation is used, and when excessive rates or incompatible materials are used.

PERSONAL SAFETY. Follow label directions exactly. Avoid splashing, spilling, leaks, spray drift, or clothing contamination. DO NOT eat, smoke, drink, or chew while using pesticides. Provide for emergency medical care in advance.

Contents

Acknowledgments

We acknowledge Steven Koike for his contribution to the section on rust diseases on caneberry. Additionally, the authors thank all of those involved in the industry of producing raspberries and blackberries who have collaborated with us on research and extension and without whom very little of the knowledge written on the following pages would be possible.

Introduction: *The Caneberry Industry*

Caneberries, including raspberries and black-berries, are growing in popularity as a fruit crop for production in California. Histori-cally, larger acreages of caneberries primarily for processing were grown in Washington and Oregon, whereas California has traditionally produced caneberries for fresh market sales. In recent years, California has led in total caneberry production overall—and in a typical year, California produces over 90 percent of the fresh market raspberries grown in the United States (USDA NASS 2010). Caneberry consumption is increasing in the United States and elsewhere around the world, and California acreage is growing in response to the rising demand (table I.1 and fig. I.1).

Table I.1. U.S. and California acreage* and value of raspberries and boysenberries, 2007–2009

Year	United States (acres)	California (acres)	Total value (California) $1,000	Total value (U.S.) $1,000
Raspberries				
2007	11,200	3,500	226,800	257,150
2008	11,100	5,400	259,200	356,252
2009	11,100	5,400	297,315	357,596
Boysenberries				
2007	810	110	845	3,051
2008	770	70	386	2,334
2009	600	†	†	1,953

Source: USDA National Agricultural Statistics Service 2010.

Note: *Acreage is for fresh sales.
†Discontinued in 2009.

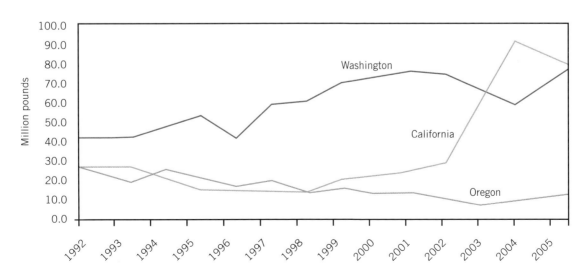

Figure I.1. Raspberry production in three major states, 1992–2005. Includes red raspberries for Washington, all for California, and red and black raspberries for Oregon. *Source:* Adapted from USDA Economic Research Serivce 2006.

Outlined below are the botanical characteristics and critical management practices for raspberries and blackberries—the principal caneberries cultivated in California.

Raspberries and blackberries may be distinguished from one another by the types of fruit they produce (figs. I.2 and I.3). Caneberry fruits are aggregate fruits, meaning that they are composed of clusters of drupelets, which are miniature fleshy fruits derived from a single carpel on the flower. In the case of the raspberry, the receptacle (which is part of the flower holding the fruit) is retained on the plant when the fruit is picked. Conversely, in blackberries (which include dewberries and boysenberries) the receptacle is removed with the fruit and there is no apparent cavity in the fruit.

Caneberries are also known as brambles because they are often thorny. Raspberries tend to have much finer thorns than blackberries. Blackberries and rarely raspberries also include genetically thornless varieties. The caneberry genus of *Rubus* includes raspberries *(Rubus idaeus)*, black raspberry *(R. occidentalis)*, dewberries *(R. ursinus)*, and many hybrids such as boysenberries, loganberries, and tayberries. Although blackberries are classified as being in the *Rubus* genus described for raspberries, the commercially important varieties belong to the subgenus *Eubatus*. Over 350 species of blackberries in the subgenus *Eubatus* have been identified, with species adapted to different regions and climates all over the world (Crandall 1994). The caneberry genus belongs to the large plant family Rosaceae, which includes apples, roses, strawberries, and caneberries.

Figure I.2. Ripe raspberry fruit (showing cavity following removal from the receptacle). *Photo:* Mark Gaskell.

Figure I.3. Ripe blackberry fruit (with the receptacle intact). *Photo:* Mark Gaskell.

Part 1 Caneberry Biology and Varieties

1 Plant Description

An important aspect of caneberries is that they have perennial crowns and root systems with biennial vegetative shoots, or canes (fig. 1.1). The canes first grow vegetatively, followed by flowering and fruiting growth. These vegetative canes are known as primocanes, while the flowering and fruiting canes are known as floricanes. Every spring new shoots, also known as suckers, form from the basal buds on the canes or from buds from the roots. These become the developing primocanes in the first year (figs. 1.2 and 1.3). Later in the summer or fall, flower buds are formed, followed by fruit either in the fall or the spring of the next year. The floricane is the second-year cane that has undergone chilling, which enables flowers and fruit to form. Once fruited, the cane senesces and is no longer capable of producing fruit, thus completing the 2-year life cycle. Primocane-bearing raspberries (and rarely also primocane-bearing blackberries) are exceptions to this description in that they are able to fruit on the first-year canes.

Figure 1.1. Bareroot raspberry plant. *Photo:* Mark Gaskell.

Figure 1.2. Early spring mowed raspberry bed showing new primocane emergence. *Photo:* Mark Gaskell.

Figure 1.3. Blackberry plant with new primocanes growing from the crown. *Photo:* Mark Gaskell.

Blackberries

Blackberries are classified by their plant growth characteristics, namely: erect, semierect, and trailing. Blackberries are typically trained onto a trellis support, although erect types occasionally can be grown without support (fig. 1.4). Erect and semierect types also produce more shoot suckers from the roots. Trailing and semierect types always require trellis support. Common examples of erect blackberries are the cultivars Apache (fig. 1.5), Chickasaw, Choctaw, and Navajo, while examples of semierect blackberries are Black Satin, Loch Ness, Chester, and Triple Crown. Trailing types of blackberries, also known as dewberries, are less common. Ollalieberry (fig. 1.6) and Siskiyou are examples of the trailing blackberries. Trailing blackberries have few to no vegetative buds on the roots, and they propagate themselves from roots formed on the tips of primocanes when they touch the soil.

Raspberries

Red Raspberry

Probably the most well-known group of caneberries is the red raspberry (fig. 1.7A). Red raspberries are composed of two main species, one being widely grown in Europe *(R. idaeus* var. *vulgatus)* and the other common in North America *(R. idaeus* var. *strigosus)*. Some productive varieties are also obtained from hybrid crosses of *R. idaeus* var. *vulgatus* and *R. idaeus* var. *strigosus.*

Black Raspberry

Black raspberry *(Rubus occidentalis)* is native to North America. Fruit flavor is stronger and the fruit is generally smaller than that of red raspberry (fig. 1.7B), and the longer canes have many stiff spines on them compared to the finer, less stiff spines or absence of spines of the red raspberry.

Figure 1.4. Semierect blackberries arranged on traditional two-wire trellis for blackberries. Note that bottom wire supports drip irrigation tubing above the bed. *Photo:* Mark Gaskell.

Figure 1.5. Apache blackberry fruit. *Photo:* Mark Bolda.

Figure 1.6. Ollalieberry. *Photo:* Mark Bolda.

Fruit on black raspberry is produced on stiff pedicels concentrated on the ends of fruiting laterals. There is little commercial production of black raspberry because there has been relatively little cultivar improvement, and the fruit quality and yield are still poor in comparison to red raspberry or blackberry.

Golden Raspberry

Golden fruited raspberry varieties *(Rubus idaeus)*, also known as yellow or amber fruited varieties, are a recessive mutation of the red raspberry, with no coloring (fig. 1.7C). They occur as both floricane- and primocane-bearing plant types.

Purple Raspberry

Purple raspberries are hybrids resulting from crossing red and black raspberry, with traits of the black raspberry being dominant. Purple raspberries are in between red and black raspberry in growth type, although the plant is more productive than black raspberries and the fruit is juicier (fig. 1.7D).

The black, purple, and yellow raspberries often receive a price premium in the marketplace compared with red raspberries or blackberries, but the volumes sold are small. They should continue to be considered more of a specialty-type small fruit, even more so than red raspberries or blackberries. As a group, these specialty berries have not received the attention from a breeding and plant improvement perspective that other small fruits have, and yields are generally lower than from the more traditional berries. Growers should plan to incorporate these into direct-sale markets, such as farm stands and farmers' markets; and as they gain experience with growing and marketing, it will become clearer if these berries have a role in larger volume shipping or wholesale sales.

Figure 1.7. Red (A), black (B), golden (C), and purple (D) raspberry fruit. *Photos:* Mark Gaskell.

Hybrid Caneberries

Several hybrid caneberries are cultivated in California that are crosses of blackberries and red raspberries. They occupy less acreage but nonetheless can be of interest to growers, especially for those who use direct marketing and wish to offer a wider variety of fruit to their customers. These caneberries are boysenberry, loganberry, and tayberry. The growth habits of these three varieties are like those of trailing blackberries, and the receptacle remains on the harvested fruit like blackberries.

Boysenberries are tolerant of warmer temperatures and can be grown in the Central Valley of California in the spring, but their season of 6 weeks or less is short (fig. 1.8A).

Loganberry *(Rubus loganobaccus)* is a large, vigorous plant, and the exceptionally flavored fruit may be eaten fresh or in jams (fig. 1.8B).

Tayberries are also a raspberry/blackberry cross that, while somewhat heat tolerant, is very rarely produced commercially. The fruit is elongated and red, and it is very soft when completely ripe. Tayberry can be recommended for pick-your-own farms, gardeners, or for making into jam.

Figure 1.8. Fruit of boysenberry (A) and loganberry (B). *Photos:* Mark Bolda.

2 Flowering and Fruit Production

There are two main fruiting types of caneberry, classified by their fruit-bearing habit: floricane bearing and primocane bearing.

Floricane Bearing

Some varieties of raspberry and virtually all varieties of blackberry grow vegetatively in the first year, followed by a period of dormancy and chilling, and then flower and fruit in the following spring and summer. These varieties are known as floricane (or summer) bearing. Some varieties may bear a small crop on the tips of the canes in the fall of the first year, but the majority of the crop in a floricane-bearing variety is produced in the second year. Examples of floricane varieties grown in California are Nova, Tulameen, and Prelude (table 2.1).

Primocane Bearing

Many raspberry varieties and a few blackberry varieties in current use bear fruit in the first year of growth on the vegetative cane (i.e., the primocane), starting at the tip and bearing fruit down to one-third to one-half of the cane in the first year. These varieties are known as primocane (or fall) bearing. Examples of primocane-bearing varieties in California are Heritage, Autumn Bliss, Autumn Britten, Caroline, and Josephine (table 2.2). Many of the proprietary varieties in use in California are also primocane bearing.

Table 2.1. Floricane-bearing red raspberries

Cultivar	Harvest period (months)	Fruit size 1 = large 5 = small	Firmness 1 = firm 5 = soft	Color 1 = dark 5 = light	Flavor 1 = strong 5 = weak	Relative production 1 = high 5 = low	Comments
Canby	June–July	4	—	—	—	2	*
Cascade Delight	—	2	2	3	1	—	*
Coho	July–Aug	3	3	3	—	—	*
Encore	July–Aug	2	—	—	—	3	*
Killarney	—	4	—	—	—	4	high chill*†
Lauren	June	2	—	—	—	4	
Malahat	—	1	2	3	—	1	*
Meeker	July–Aug	3	3	3	—	—	—
Nova	May–June	2	2	4	3	3	—
Prelude	June–July	2	2	3	3	3	—
Titan	—	1	—	—	—	2	high chill*†
Tulameen	July–Sept	1	2	3	—	4	NW U.S.; European standard; high chill†
Willamette	June–July	3	3	2	3	3	—

Notes:
*Not extensively evaluated in California.
†Many floricane-bearing raspberries require more chilling than primocane-bearing varieties. Their production is more uncertain in mild temperature fruit production areas of California and the harvest period is more variable.

Table 2.2. Primocane-bearing red raspberries

Cultivar	Harvest period (months)	Fruit size 1 = large 5 = small	Firmness 1 = firm 5 = soft	Color 1 = dark 5 = light	Flavor 1 = strong 5 = weak	Relative production 1 = high 5 = low	Comments
Autumn Bliss	May–Dec†	3	3	3	3	2	widely adapted; productive; fruit may be soft
Autumn Britten	May–Dec	3–4	2	3	3	2	similar to Autumn Bliss; firmer fruit
Caroline	June–Dec	2	2	3	3	2	widely adapted; productive; firm fruit; shows some susceptibility to sunburn
Dinkum	June–Sept	3	3	3	4	3	shorter season
Erika	June–Dec	2	2	3	2	2	new; widely planted in Europe
Heritage	July–Nov	2	2	3	2	3	longtime standard CA shipping cultivar
Himbo Top	July–Sept	2	2	3	3	4	new; early fruit is off color*
Joan J	July–Sept	2	2	1	3	2	new*
Josephine	June–Dec	3	3	3	3	4	low primocane production
Polana	June–Sept	4	3	2	3	4	*
Polka	June–Dec	2	2	3	2	2	new; widely planted in Europe
Ruby	June–Sept	3	3	3	4	4	berries held tightly*
Summit	June–Sept	4	3	3	3	3	slow to establish

Notes:
*Not extensively evaluated in California.
†Production season with primocane varieties can be long if two-spotted mites are controlled.

Varieties differ in their overall adaptation to growing conditions, productivity, and plant growth type, as well as many other horticultural characteristics. There are many different parameters for growers to consider when selecting caneberry varieties for production. The most important characteristics for growers, after production and overall vigor, are related to fruit quality. Flavor and color are important to all growers. For example, a red raspberry that is too pale may lack consumer acceptance because it is thought to be immature, whereas a variety that is too dark may be considered overripe.

Raspberries are extremely perishable and have one of the most limited postharvest shelf lives of any fruit. Growers who ship to distant points via wholesale markets are likewise interested in firm fruit that will withstand several days in the marketing stream. Growers who sell directly through farm stands and farmers' markets are not as concerned with firmness as wholesale shippers, but even they need reasonably firm fruit that will hold a few days in storage and survive a minimum level of handling. No single variety is ideal for all situations, so growers should make their selection based on features most vital to their operations.

Variety improvement programs are constantly developing new varieties through plant breeding. Numerous plant breeding programs dedicated to

Figure 3.1. Josephine red raspberry. *Photo:* Mark Bolda.

producing and distributing publicly available varieties (fig. 3.1) have been replaced by private breeders or grower/shippers who produce proprietary varieties and patent them, often restricting distribution of those varieties. Increasingly, growers do not have access to potentially productive and valuable varieties, and the selection of publicly available varieties is limited. Also, in some instances public varieties developed in Europe or New Zealand may have a 1- to 2-year quarantine period before they can be distributed in the United States. As a result, more recent releases have not been trialed in the United States, or they have been replaced by superior varieties in Europe before they are available in the United States.

Yellow or Golden Raspberry Varieties

Anne

Released by the University of Maryland breeding program (now privatized as Five Aces Breeding). Fruit is large with good conical shape (fig. 3.2). Fairly susceptible to fruit rot. Does not produce many primocanes for a continuing crop. Excellent sweet fruit flavor, beginning to ripen several weeks before Heritage.

Goldie

Similar characteristics to Heritage red raspberry, with comparable yields. Changes to pink-orange as it ripens. Fruit is of good size and quality. Fruit can dull over time after picked.

Kiwigold

Similar characteristics to Heritage red raspberry, with comparable or lower yields. Plants reported as self-supporting. Fruit actually has a peachlike color, is of good size and good quality, with sweet flavor.

Figure 3.2. Anne variety yellow raspberry. *Photo:* Mark Bolda.

Purple Raspberry Varieties

Brandywine

Very long canes, with prominent thorns. Relatively resistant to caneberry diseases. Nonspreading; plants sucker only from the base. Late-ripening fruit with strong flavor, often used for jams and jellies. Fruit is large and reddish purple.

Royalty

Popular and well-known purple raspberry variety (fig. 3.3). Canes are very long and vigorous,

forming a hedge as other raspberries do. High yields of large, good-tasting fruit. Fruit is soft and may be difficult to ship.

Figure 3.3. Royalty variety purple raspberry. *Photo:* Mark Bolda.

Black Raspberry Varieties

Munger

Fruit is shiny, firm, and good tasting. Munger has medium plant vigor and production.

Jewel

Plants are vigorous and productive. Erect growth habit. More disease resistant than other black raspberry varieties. Glossy, black fruit with strong raspberry flavor, ripening in midsummer. Good flavor and an excellent choice for jams and jellies.

Mac Black

Ripens after Jewel and continues to produce to the late season. Mac Black produces good-sized, good-flavored berries. The long canes of this black raspberry will benefit from a trellis system.

Proprietary Varieties

There are many proprietary primocane-bearing varieties of red raspberry in California that have been developed by private farming or marketing companies and whose propagation and distribution are strictly controlled by the owner of the patent. These varieties normally are not available for sale to growers without production arrangements with the company owning the patent. Growers of these varieties should seek advice from the distributor on plant and fruiting characteristics, as well as guidelines for their cultivation. (See table 3.1 for blackberry variety information.)

Table 3.1. Blackberry varieties

Cultivar	Harvest period (months)	Fruit size 1 = large 5 = small	Firmness 1 = firm 5 = soft	Flavor 1 = good 5 = poor	Relative production 1 = high 5 = low	Comments
Apache	June–July	4	3	3	3	fruit can be seedy; ships well
Chester	July–Oct	3	4	4	1	not easily shipped when fully mature
Chickasaw	June–July	1	3	2	3	very thorny cane; fruit softens toward end of season
Choctaw	May–June	2	3	3	3	very thorny cane; fruit softens toward end of season
Kiowa	June–July	1	3	3	2	very thorny cane; fruit one of the largest
Loch Ness	July–Aug	3	3	4	3	—
Navajo	June–July	3	3	1	3	—
Obsidian	May–June	3	3	3	3	—
Ollalieberry	May–June	3	4	1	2	not easily shipped; fruit appearance is rumpled
Prime-Ark	July-Dec	2	2	2	2	primocane-bearing variety; for best results, mow plants to ground in winter and tip plants at 18 in following emergence
Ouachita	June–July	2	3	3	2	excellent shipping characteristics
Prime-Jan, Prime-Jim	Aug–Nov	2	3	3	2	primocane-bearing blackberry; canes very thorny; for best results in California, plants should be tipped at 3 ft tall, and branches again at 5–6 ft
Siskiyou	June	4	3	3	4	—
Triple Crown	July–Aug	2	5	4	2	fruit does not ripen evenly; tip is immature while rest of fruit is fully ripe

4 Macro-Tunnel and Field Management

Caneberry Production in Macro-Tunnels

The use of macro-tunnels, also known as Spanish tunnels or high tunnels, has become popular as one way of obtaining higher yield and yield in the off-season production periods (late fall through winter), since prices for quality raspberry fruit during this time of year are typically high (figs. 4.1A and B). The use of tunnels theoretically enables the production of raspberries 12 months per year in the mild climates of the coastal growing areas. Tunnels typically raise the average temperature by 6° to 10°F.

Macro-tunnels are semipermanent constructions built from 8- to 10-foot-long anchor posts spaced from 10 to 12 feet apart on either side, linked by arches spanning three or four rows of caneberries (approximately 21 to 28 feet wide). (For equivalents between U.S. and metric systems of measurement, see the conversion table at the end of this publication.) Growers generally construct the hoops using galvanized steel pipe and a bending machine to put in the curve (fig. 4.2). Tunnels themselves are 10 to 12 feet high. Clear polyethylene plastic sheeting is stretched over this construction and is rolled up or down depending on weather and needs of the grower (fig. 4.3).

In the most common production system in California, primocane-bearing varieties of raspberry are grown under macro-tunnels for one fall and one spring-to-summer harvest. Plants are planted and grown in the first spring and covered with the tunnels in mid to late summer. Plants produce fruit on the tops of canes beginning in October or November and produce until February or March. The fruited tops are removed, with 3 to 4 feet of cane remaining at the end of the growing season.

Figure 4.1. Raspberry production in tunnels: outside view (A) and inside view (B). *Photos:* Mark Bolda.

Figure 4.2. View of tunnel structure showing inside view of pipe structure. *Photo:* Mark Bolda.

Figure 4.3. Outside view of overall tunnel structure with stretched plastic. *Photo:* Mark Bolda.

Flowering and harvest begin anew on remaining canes the following August. This is the system that predominates in Central and Southern California for winter production. In the Watsonville area, the production period is concentrated in late summer or fall. The fruited tops of the canes are removed in early winter; the canes become productive again in the early spring, and they are generally harvested until June. To avoid the damaging effects of wind and rain in the winter season, the plastic covering the tunnels is removed. At the completion of this harvest, plants are removed and ground is prepared for the next crop.

Macro-tunnels are best suited to mild coastal areas, where there are not wide variations in diurnal temperatures, unlike in more inland areas. In those areas where temperatures rise above 80° to 90°F, tunnels will need to be vented regularly during the day and then closed down again prior to sunset. Large numbers of fieldworkers are required in such situations just to manage temperature in the tunnels, and the associated costs may be prohibitive.

The combination of field production and covered, macro-tunnel production in different growing areas from San Diego to Watsonville permits the production of raspberries year-round in California. Larger farming and marketing companies are now producing raspberries for year-round market availability, with diverse farming operations in a range of growing areas. Off-shore production in Mexico, Guatemala, and Chile will supplement fruit availability during off-season periods.

Site Selection, Field Layout, and Soils

Sites for raspberry and blackberry production will ideally be level, deep, and well drained, with soils containing 1 to 3 percent organic matter. Raspberries and blackberries can both be adapted to more difficult site conditions, with precautions for providing the elements critical for optimum growth. Caneberries are easiest to manage on level land, but they can be adapted to slopes if care is taken to prevent erosion and to provide the plants with adequate nutrition, moisture, and drainage. Avoid sites with a high water table; raised beds should be used in soils that are high in clay or slow to drain.

Windy sites should be avoided when selecting sites for caneberries, or windbreaks should be used to protect the field. Wind increases evaporative demand and interferes with moisture uniformity, which is important for consistent flowering and fruit development. Scraping and scarring of canes, leaves, and fruit is a more direct and serious problem associated with windy conditions. Good air circulation is generally desirable because well-ventilated areas aid the rapid, early drying of foliage and fruit, and those sites are not conducive to the infestation of many diseases. Fields should receive full sun throughout the day for best fruit quality and yields.

Areas of Adaptation

There are cultivars of both raspberries and blackberries that will grow in any part of California. More northern areas and more inland and desert areas have a narrower group of adapted varieties and a shorter harvest season. This is because cold temperatures limit production in winter and excessive heat slows flowering and fruit production during peak summer months. Heat also has an adverse effect on fruit quality, particularly with raspberries. Inland or desert areas will have short (3- to 6-week) harvest seasons in spring or early summer. Blackberries overall tolerate hot summers more than raspberries, and some varieties will keep flowering and producing during warm weather. Fruit quality suffers during warm weather, however, as berries are frequently smaller and less firm.

A wider range of cultivars is suitable for growing in mild coastal areas, and the moderate temperatures contribute to flowering and fruiting over an extended production period. In the mild coastal conditions, winter temperatures typically do not fall enough to induce dormancy and summer temperatures are not high enough to affect flowering or fruit quality. Coastal production areas are able to combine cultivar(s) and appropriate cultural practices for a harvest season that can extend for 6 months or longer. Combined with the use of macro-tunnels, this production period may be shifted into more profitable harvest windows.

Chill hours (hours of cold conditioning) are not a critical factor with primocane-bearing raspberries, as chilling is not a requirement for fruiting on primocanes. Most coastal and southern California growing areas receive adequate chill hours for a large number of the newer blackberry cultivars. Chilling is more important, however, for floricane-bearing cultivars. Chill hours and the consistency and timing of chilling and harvest determine the usefulness of floricane-bearing cultivars in different areas. In more northern areas or in the mountains and foothills, chill hours are sufficient for most of the floricane types, and the harvest period is more restricted due to the temperature regime. The floricane group of cultivars, although they have a more restricted adaptation and harvest window, may be valuable because they fill important market niches or have better shipping quality than primocane types harvested during that period.

Cold air drains to low areas and slows early plant development and ripening (fig. 4.4). Low-lying areas and valley bottoms should be avoided where early production is desirable. Plantings for production targeting early-season market windows should be on south-facing slopes with mild conditions, typical along the coast, or within protected cropping structures such as macro-tunnels. Early production also carries additional risk, as early flowering on south-facing slopes may result in flowers or fruit being lost to late-season radiative frosts. In coastal growing areas, frosts are infrequent and light, so the effect on overall growth and development is minor.

Site Preparation

Caneberries will tolerate heavier-textured, relatively poorly drained soils if irrigation is managed appropriately and if planted on raised beds to improve internal aeration and drainage. Both raspberries and blackberries are susceptible to root rot diseases that will debilitate the planting over time if care is not taken to provide adequate drainage. Soil sites with a history of Verticillium or Phytophthora root rot problems should be fumigated and bedded prior to planting, but even these practices may not be adequate to avoid disease problems with susceptible cultivars. Although hillside land presents few drainage problems generally, with heavier soils it is advisable to use raised-bed terraces or contours on hillside land as well as on more level areas.

Caneberries also tolerate very sandy soils if care is taken to provide the appropriate amount and distribution of water by irrigation and to provide for the nutritional needs of the plants with a managed fertilization program. There are benefits to applying

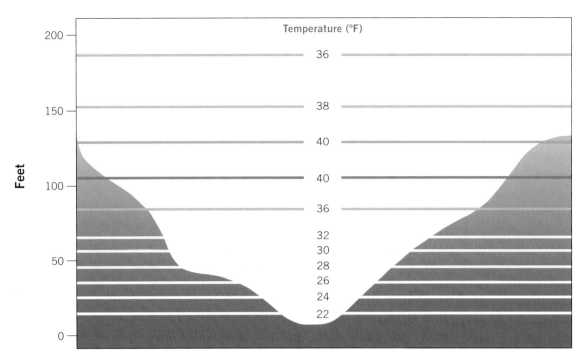

Figure 4.4. Temperature variation with slope position. *Source:* Adapted from Snyder 1994.

organic amendments to increase the organic matter of sandy soils, but amounts and cost vary widely. Organic matter improves water-holding capacity and nutrient availability in sandy soils, but amendment application costs should be compared to fertilizer and irrigation costs.

Land preparation prior to planting may require deep ripping of suspected hardpan soils as well as preparing the raised beds. Bed height of 6 to 8 inches is adequate for most soil conditions. Caneberries are planted on raised beds in all cases except sandy soils. Planting on beds protects plants from diseases and poor vigor associated with poorly drained soils, and there are no adverse effects from planting on beds.

Soils should be analyzed prior to planting for pH, phosphorus, potassium, calcium, magnesium, and the micronutrients sulfur, iron, zinc, boron, molybdenum, and manganese. If high sodium or salt accumulation is suspected, soils should also be analyzed for electrical conductivity (EC) and

sodium absorption ratio (SAR). Preplant application and incorporation of granular nutrients is the most economical way of correcting nutrient deficiencies. The nitrogen (N) nutrient needs can be supplied on a regular basis during periods when plants are actively growing.

Establishment of a cover crop may be useful in conditions where it is desirable to increase soil organic matter if at least 5 to 6 months is available prior to planting. For example, the organic matter provided by a vigorous cover crop will improve water-holding capacity and nutrient retention. The cover crop mix is planted, and following 5 to 6 months of growth, it is mowed, chopped, and incorporated prior to bed preparation. A permanent inter-row cover crop may also be planted during the rainy season once the planting is established. A non-invasive grass, legume, or mixed ground cover crop between rows prevents erosion and dust but may require supplemental irrigation. Mixes of bunch grasses are available commercially for planting between rows of caneberries.

When establishing caneberries on sloping land, be careful to establish the plantings on a contour with hedgerows on no more than a 3 percent slope. Hillsides often have shallower soils, with more variable fertility, organic matter, and physical properties across the hillside. A cover crop or additional compost or other source of organic matter can be applied prior to planting to make the soil's fertility and physical properties more uniform. Cultivating on hillsides often leads to the formation of terraces and may contribute to the downhill movement of soil. Caneberries can be managed without the need for inter-row cultivation by mowing inter-rows and thus avoiding soil movement on hillside plantings.

Row orientation has a minimal effect on caneberry production. North-to-south row orientation generally has more even light distribution, and fruit will be more uniformly distributed on both sides of the hedge in such an orientation. Some shading from east-to-west-running rows occurs in winter, and these rows may have more sunburned fruit in summer on the south-facing side. In practice, however, field shape often determines the row orientation, and other cultural practices are probably just as important as row orientation in determining yield and fruit quality.

Planting

Beds may be treated with registered preplant herbicides or fumigants for disease and weed control. Fumigants may be necessary in fields with a history of Verticillium wilt or Phytophthora root rot. An alternative method for controlling weeds during the establishment period is with delayed seedbed preparation. With this technique, beds are prepared 4 to 8 weeks prior to planting and irrigated thoroughly. Weeds are allowed to germinate on the bed surface, and then they are killed with a nonselective herbicide such as glyphosate. A crop flamer can be used to kill weeds in organic plantings. If time allows, an additional flush of weeds is allowed to germinate over a 2- to 3-week period and then the weeds are treated with a nonselective herbicide or flaming. For planting, the bed soil is only disturbed for the planting hole or for a narrow furrow to plant root

pieces. This minimizes bringing new weed seeds to the surface for germination. The area between and around plants can be mulched with wood waste or other organic materials.

Plants are typically available from nurseries as 1-year-old dormant canes, as root sections, or as tissue-cultured greenhouse plug transplants. The 1-year-old canes of primocane-bearing raspberry types will produce some initial fruit in 4 to 5 months from planting.

The hedgerow eventually fills in completely, regardless of plant spacing. Yields after the second or third year are the same, regardless of how closely plants are spaced initially (fig. 4.5).

Figure 4.5. Raspberry solid hedge with no individual plants apparent. *Photo:* Mark Bolda.

Floricane-bearing raspberries and most blackberries (with the exception of the recently released primocane-bearing types) will require 1 year of vegetative growth prior to the first fruit harvest in the second year. Root sections will require 5 to 6 months to begin production in mild areas or under high tunnels, and they tend to begin production all at the same time. Small transplants from tissue culture, such as those often used for blackberries, require one whole season of vegetative growth to become established, and fruiting will begin the second year. Roots are most often planted in a solid line of pieces in furrows 4 to 6 inches deep. Thicker, more highly branched root pieces have a higher establishment percentage than thinner pieces and can be planted at lower density. Roots are often sold in 25-pound boxes, and 15 to 17 boxes will be sufficient to plant 1 acre.

In-row plant spacing for raspberries typically varies from 1 to 3 feet. These plants will eventually spread to fill an entire hedgerow, so early yields (years 1 to 3) will depend on plant spacing. Closer spacing will mean higher costs for the establishment year but higher early yields. For the highest, earliest yields from canes or plants of primocane-bearing types, the plants should be spaced 1 foot or less apart in the row. After 2 to 3 years, the yields should be similar despite differences in in-row plant spacing. Cane-planted plots can be used with root-planted plots, along with the pruning of older plots, to extend the harvest season and stay in the market for a long season.

Blackberry in-row spacing varies from 3 to 4 feet depending on cultivar type, but blackberries will maintain the initial plant spacing throughout the life of the crop (fig. 4.6). Closer plant spacing is used for more upright, erect-type cultivars and the wider spacing for trailing-type cultivars. Early yields with blackberries are directly related to plant size at establishment. Smaller plants from tissue culture require the first one or two seasons, depending on the length of the growing season, to establish and reach productive size.

Figure 4.6. Spaced blackberry plants with branch from the crown base. *Photo:* Mark Gaskell.

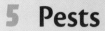

5 Pests

All of the following pests in caneberries are discussed in the UC IPM guidelines, with periodically updated pesticide information. Please refer to the caneberry section of the UC IPM website for information updates regarding these pests: http://www.ipm.ucdavis.edu/PMG/select-newpest.caneberry.html.

Insects

Redberry Mite

The eriophyid mite (*Acalitus essigi* (Hassan)) is a serious pest of commercially produced blackberries in California. *A. essigi*, commonly known as the redberry mite, overwinters within dormant buds of blackberries. The redberry mite is microscopic, requiring at least a 20X hand lens for detection. As the season progresses, redberry mite migration occurs up the flower pedicel to colonize leaf axial bracts, the fruit's calyx area, and the spaces between berry drupelets. Redberry mite feeding prevents berries from ripening uniformly, causing several or many drupelets to remain as a bright red cluster on the otherwise black and fully ripe fruit (fig. 5.1). Affected drupelets never do ripen, causing the entire fruit to be inedible and unmarketable. Historically, in the Monterey Bay production area of California, redberry mite has been most damaging to blackberry varieties that mature later in the summer (August and September). Commercial blackberry growers estimate that redberry mites can cause 10 to 50 percent or more loss in total yields.

Horticultural oils give significant control of redberry mite, while causing the least harm to fruit yield, when used at the rate of 1.2 to 2 percent volume oil to volume water and applied after the green fruit or first pink fruit stage in four consecutive applications spaced 2 or 3 weeks apart. Complete plant canopy coverage is important when using horticultural oils, so a minimum of 50 gallons of water per acre is recommended.

Figure 5.1. Redberry mite in blackberry. Note how fruit in front is half red and half black. *Photo:* Mark Bolda.

The potential for phytotoxicity of oil products or oil product mixes has not been fully evaluated for all blackberry varieties in all growing areas. Small-plot tests may be prudent to determine safety margins for particular blackberry varieties for specific environmental conditions in different growing areas.

Note that oil and sulfur products should never be tank-mixed, due to risk of phytotoxicity. If oils are used after or before sulfur products, be sure to observe all recommended label precautions.

Two-Spotted Spider Mite

The two-spotted spider mite *(Tetranychus urticae)* can be a serious pest of caneberries, especially in caneberries cultivated in warm areas or under macro-tunnels. The two-spotted mite reduces yield potential of the plant, even at low levels of infestation.

Two-spotted spider mites infest the undersides of caneberry leaves, where they may form colonies and produce light webbing when abundant (fig. 5.2). Two-spotted spider mites are very small, barely visible to the naked eye. Nymphs, adult males, and reproductive females range from green to a yellowish hue in color. Reproductively dormant females are bright orange. Under a hand lens, two dark blotches appear on either side of the adult two-spotted spider mite's body, with two red eyespots toward the head.

Figure 5.2. Raspberry leaf infested with two-spotted spider mite. *Photo:* Mark Bolda.

In areas where temperatures are cold in winter, two-spotted spider mites overwinter as dormant adult females at the base of the caneberry plants or weeds in and around the field. With the onset of warm weather, these mites migrate to the caneberry foliage and begin to lay eggs. In the mild winters of the coastal growing regions of California, it is unusual for a high percentage of mites to become dormant; instead they continue to grow and lay eggs through the winter, although at a slower pace than in summer. The complete life cycle, under ideal conditions of hot, dry weather, can take place in 10 days.

The key to successful management of two-spotted spider mites is to monitor populations and to initiate control measures in a timely manner. Once populations are large, much damage has been done to the potential yield of the plant, and they are more difficult to control than smaller populations.

Currently there are few miticides registered for control of two-spotted mite in caneberries. Research suggests that application of miticides should be made earlier in the year, when mite populations are lower, since earlier application can result in longer control and less yield loss. While moderately effective, agricultural oils, petroleum, and vegetable and neem oil compounds are another option for mite control. When using chemical controls, it is important to know that coverage is very important, and volumes of 200 gallons water per acre may be needed for adequate distribution. In many cases, especially with the spray oils, mites that escape contact with the control material will survive.

A biological control agent often used for control of the two-spotted mite is the predatory mite *Phytoseiulus persimilis. P. persimilis* does best in temperatures of 60° to 80° F and does not do well above 100° F. Growers are to be cautioned that even in low numbers, at densities below those controlled by *P. persimilis*, two-spotted spider mites can reduce yield potential of caneberries.

No precise treatment thresholds have been established for two-spotted mites in caneberries. Monitor to keep track of increasing pest mite populations as well as predatory mite populations. A ratio of 1 predator to 10 two-spotted mites is considered favorable for biological control.

Normal pruning of primocanes and removal of dead floricanes in caneberries can reduce the buildup of two-spotted spider mites. Controlling dust by watering or oiling surrounding roads is an important factor in limiting two-spotted spider mite populations.

Raspberry Crown Borer

The raspberry crown borer, *Pennisetia marginata*, affects raspberries and blackberries. The adult raspberry crown borer is a clearwing moth resembling a yellow jacket wasp (fig. 5.3). It has a wingspan of about 1 inch and has a black body with four yellow, horizontal stripes on the abdomen as well as stripes on the thorax. The legs are yellow and, unlike the short antennae of a yellow jacket wasp, the antennae of the raspberry crown borer are feathery, long, and curving outward from the head.

The raspberry crown borer takes 2 years to complete its life cycle, beginning in late summer when the female raspberry crown borer moth lays reddish brown eggs on the undersides of caneberry leaflets. Once hatched, larvae migrate to the base of the caneberry plant, where they either dig into the base of the cane and form a sheath out of plant material or find a protected area in the bark and stay there for the winter. In spring of the following year, the larvae burrow galleries through the crown of the plant and continue to do so through the first summer. The second winter is spent in the roots, and larvae continue to burrow into the roots and crown during the following summer. Larvae undergo a short pupation period of 2 to 3 weeks in the burrow within the crown in late June and July, and they emerge as adult moths in late July to early August. Adult moths are active from early August to late September and may be seen during the day resting on foliage.

A caneberry plant that is infested with raspberry crown borer larvae will begin to wither and visibly wilt because of the physical damage to vascular tissue, especially in the second year of infestation. A hole at the base of the plant in the crown, with sawdustlike frass at the entrance, is also indicative of raspberry crown borer activity (fig. 5.4).

The best way to manage the raspberry crown borer is to prevent its intrusion into the caneberry field through cultural controls. The use of clean planting stock is necessary to reduce the movement of infested plant stock from one field to another. Secondly, it is important to be mindful of populations of wild caneberries surrounding the planting, especially blackberries, because these plants will support populations of raspberry crown borer.

Leaf Rollers

Four species of leaf rollers—the orange tortrix *(Agyrotaenia citrana)*, the oblique-banded leaf roller *(Choristoneura rosaceana)*, the light brown apple moth *(Epiphyas postvittana)*, and the apple pandemis *(Pandemis pyrusana)*—are pests of caneberries in California.

Leaf roller larvae generally will find a leaf or group of leaves and roll them together, hence the name. However, the larvae may also be found in and between fruit and flowers. The main problem with

Figure 5.3. Mature raspberry crown borer. *Photo:* Mark Bolda.

Figure 5.4. Holes in base of blackberry canes left by larvae of raspberry crown borer. *Photo:* Mark Bolda.

leaf rollers (with the exception of the light brown apple moth, which is a regulated pest) is that they can contaminate harvested fruit, especially when present in larger infestations. The emerging adults in late April to mid-May are the ones that produce the generation of larvae infesting fruit at harvest.

The orange tortrix has two or three generations per year, and it most often overwinters as a larva in dead leaves on canes in caneberry fields, rather than the surrounding area. The oblique-banded leaf roller has two generations per year and is found overwintering under bud and bark scales. While the life cycle of the light brown apple moth has not yet been thoroughly resolved, it is suspected to also have two generations per year. The apple pandemis also has two generations per year, and it tends to be more numerous in cooler years and cooler locations.

The adult moth of the orange tortrix is a small, ¼- to ½-inch-long, bell-shaped moth (fig. 5.5). The male moth has an orange to tan blotched coloration with diagonal brown bands, while the female is the same color with a dark blotch on the inner wing margin. Hind wings, seen when the moth is in flight, are white. As with several other leaf rollers, larvae have a bright green body with a tan head.

Adult oblique-banded leaf roller moths are tan with alternating light and dark brown bands across their forewings. Eggs are greenish yellow, flattened, and laid in overlapping masses. Larvae are green in color, can be longer than 1 inch at maturity, and can be difficult to distinguish.

Light brown apple moth larvae look similar to those of other leaf rollers. The adults, ¼- to ½-inch long, have variable patterns of dark brown on the wings. However, males may be distinguished from those of other leaf rollers by an extension of the outer wing. The life cycle of the light brown apple moth is not yet well known in California.

Apple pandemis moths are orange to rust colored and have a blotchy pattern on their forewings. Larvae are very difficult to distinguish from those of the light brown apple moth and orange tortrix.

In contrast to the other leaf rollers, the light brown apple moth is currently a regulated pest, and control measures to obtain complete control of this pest are strongly recommended. It is suggested to start management programs for the light brown apple moth early in the season, when numbers are low, larvae are small, and the caneberry hedgerow is easily penetrated by spray. However, absent regulatory mandates, the approach to reduce infestation risk of the light brown apple moth in caneberries should be similar to the approach to reduce other tortricid pests.

Leaf rollers are especially common in blackberries, and growers should monitor their crops for any totricid infestation by looking for evidence of larvae, pupae, pupal cases, webbing, and feeding damage at least 10 days prior to the commencement of harvest (fig. 5.6). All pesticide applications will be more effective when targeted at the young, early instars of tortricid larvae. Since generations can overlap, it may be useful for growers to spray regularly if evidence of tortricids continues to be found during the season.

Infestation risk can also be substantially reduced by proper field management of caneberry

Figure 5.5. Orange tortrix adults and egg mass. *Photo:* Jack Kelly Clark, courtesy UC IPM.

Figure 5.6. Leaf roller emerging from leaf roll on blackberry. *Photo:* Mark Bolda.

crops. Most overwintering tortricid larvae survive in surrounding weeds or in trash on and beneath the hedgerow, so these should be removed or disked into the ground.

There are many predators, including lacewings, damsel bugs, and minute pirate bugs, along with many species of spiders, that prey on leaf rollers. In combination with parasitoids such as *Trichogramma* species, there can be significant reduction of leaf roller larvae and eggs by these biological control mechanisms. Growers should be aware of these before applying chemical controls.

Yellow Jackets

Yellow jackets are yellow and black (or white and black) wasps belonging to the subgenus *Vespula*. In California, yellow jackets generally build nests in existing cavities, such as rodent burrows and hollow logs. These nests can become very large by late summer or fall and may contain up to 1,000 wasps.

Yellow jackets are attracted to ripe and injured raspberry fruit for their moisture and sugar, especially during the latter part of the season. They are very bothersome to pickers, since they are aggressive and have a painful sting.

Keeping the field clean is the key to managing yellow jackets. Maintaining plants clear of overripe fruit as well as prompt harvesting of ripe fruit will decrease the attractiveness of the field to yellow jackets. There are a variety of traps available for controlling yellow jackets around working areas.

Sap Beetles

Also known as picnic beetles, sap beetles that infest caneberries are of two species, *Glischrochilus quadrisignatus* and *Glischrochilus fasciatus*. The adult beetles, which bore into the caneberry fruit as well as contaminate harvested fruit, measure about ¼ inch in length. They are a shiny black, with two small yellow spots on the back of each wing cover. The antennae are distinctively knobbed. Larvae are about the same length as adults, with a brown head capsule. Larvae are not often found inside fruit.

Since sap beetle adults are often inside fruit, pesticide application is not very useful nor very often recommended. However, sap beetle infestation can be limited by removing overripe and damaged fruit in a timely manner. Fruit should be completely removed from the field to avoid attracting sap beetles

to the general area. Covering harvested fruit is another way to reduce contamination by sap beetles.

Leafhoppers

There are two species of leafhoppers infesting caneberries in California: the white apple leafhopper (*Typhlocyba pomaria*) and the rose leafhopper (*Edwardsiana rosae*). Both damage caneberries by sucking chloroplasts out of the cells in the leaf, resulting in a white stippling on the surface. This can cause some reduction in yield potential. Additionally, leafhoppers produce tiny specks of black excrement, which, when deposited on fruit, results in lower marketability.

Both species of leafhoppers overwinter as eggs, and the rose leafhopper has three generations per year, while the white apple leafhopper has two generations per year. There is significant predation of leafhoppers by green lacewings and minute pirate bugs, as well as some parasitization of the eggs. However, in the case of high populations, it can be beneficial to apply an insecticide.

Root Weevils

Four species of weevils can be found in California caneberries. They are cribrate weevil (*Otiorhychus cribicollis*), black vine weevil (*Otiorhychus sulcatus*), Fuller rose weevil (*Asynonychus godmani*), and the woods weevil (*Nemocestes incomptus*). All four species of weevils are flightless, and they hide around the crowns of the plant during the day and come out to feed on foliage at night. Adults emerge in spring through early summer, egg laying takes place midsummer, and the weevils overwinter as larvae. Weevil larvae feed on roots, are dormant in the winter, begin feeding again in the spring, pupate, and emerge as adults in the spring to early summer.

While the adult root weevils are easiest to find because of their exposure out in the open, their feeding is not really harmful to plants. It is the larval feeding on the roots and tunneling into plant crowns that cause damage. The feeding on the roots leads to inhibited water conduction and a wilting, weakened plant, with death occurring in some cases.

Weevils are not easy to manage in caneberries. Growers may remove plants apparently infested and continue to remove plants in a circular fashion around infested plants until larvae or pupae are no longer found. As weevils are flightless, they cannot travel very far from the original infestation. Fields should be fumigated between caneberry plantings, and new plantings should be situated at least 1,000 feet from plantings known to be infested with weevils.

Raspberry Horntail

The raspberry horntail *(Hartigia cressoni)* is a wood wasp and only occasionally seen in California caneberries. The adults are up to ¾ inch long, with the females showing more yellow and black, while the males are mostly black. The larvae, which grow from eggs deposited near the tip of the cane, girdle the tips of the cane, causing weakening and occasional breakage. Later the larvae feed their way into the terminal part of the cane, often causing dieback. Overwintering of larvae is done farther down into the pith of the cane in a silken cavity. After pupation, adults emerge in the following spring through a hole in the cane.

Chemical control is often not necessary. Canes exhibiting horntail activity should be removed and destroyed to prevent the larvae from completing their life cycle. There are also several ichneumonid wasps that parasitize raspberry horntail larvae.

Greenhouse Whitefly

Greenhouse whiteflies *(Trialerodes vaporariorum)* can occasionally become a serious problem in California caneberries. Development of the greenhouse whitefly from egg to adult takes as little as 18 days if temperatures and host plant conditions are ideal. Ideal temperatures for fastest development are between 80° and 90°F. Adult whiteflies are most commonly found in large numbers on the primocane growth of caneberries, and they fly up when the leaves of those canes are disturbed.

Greenhouse whitefly adults lay masses of minute, elliptical eggs on the undersides of leaves. After hatching, the whitefly larva goes through four instars of development, the last of which is often called the pupal stage and is most identifiable by red eyes and long, waxy filaments around the margin of the body. The adult emerges from this stage and is a tiny, white insect 0.06 inch long. It has four membranous wings that are held parallel to the top of the body and covered with white wax. The wings partially fold over one another.

Since no whitefly-transmitted viruses have been identified in California caneberries, damage from this pest is limited to feeding and the exudation of honeydew. Heavy feeding can reduce plant vigor, and honeydew exudates not only leave fruit sticky but also create a substrate for growth of black mold.

This reduces photosynthetic function of leaves and renders fruit unmarketable.

While biological control of whiteflies via predators and parasitoids is useful with low populations, moderate to large populations are better managed through the use of pesticides.

Vinegar Flies

Vinegar flies *(Drosophila* spp.) are small, brown to yellow flies, generally attracted to fermenting fruit of all kinds. Adults are small (2 to 3 mm), with red eyes, a pale brown thorax and abdomen, and black stripes on the abdomen. Eggs and larvae of vinegar flies are a contamination problem of very ripe or overripe fruit, and adult flies can be a nuisance when numerous.

Another species of vinegar fly, spotted-wing drosophila *(Drosophila suzukii),* was discovered infesting ripening cherry, raspberry, blackberry, blueberry, and strawberry crops in California in 2008. While adults and maggots of spotted-wing drosophila closely resemble the common vinegar fly, they damage fruit that is yet to be harvested, rather than overripe or rotten fruit.

The most distinguishable trait of the spotted-wing drosophila adult is that the males have a black spot toward the tip of each wing (fig. 5.7). Larvae are tiny (up to 3.5 mm), white, cylindrical maggots. One or many larvae may be found feeding within a single fruit. After maturing, the larvae partially or completely exit the fruit to pupate.

Figure 5.7. *Drosophila suzukii* adult male. *Photo:* Martin Hauser, courtesy UC IPM.

At this point not much is known about the life cycle of spotted-wing drosophila in California; however, like other vinegar flies, it appears to have a short life cycle (1 or 2 weeks, depending on temperature) and may have as many as 10 generations per year. This rapid developmental rate allows it to quickly develop large populations and inflict severe damage to a crop.

Adult flies may be captured throughout much of the year, but they are most active at 68°F; activity becomes reduced at temperatures above 86°F, and adult males become sterile.

While no set management program has yet been determined for spotted-wing drosophila, a successful one will need to focus on controlling flies before they lay eggs, as well as reducing breeding sites. There are no effective tools for controlling maggots within fruit. Three essential parts of a management program include the consistent use of attractant bait sprays or pesticides, in-field sanitation and removal of rotten fruit, and an area-wide management program to prevent a single, heavily infested field from reinfesting other areas where consistent treatment is occurring.

Soil Diseases

There are several important soil pathogens of caneberries, and raspberries are especially sensitive to several of them.

Phytophthora Root Rot

Phytophthora root rot is a disease caused by several species of *Phytophthora*, of which the most common in caneberries is *Phytophthora fragariae*. Phytophthora is commonly found in areas of a field that remain saturated for periods of time, such as low areas and areas with clay soils or leaking irrigation lines. Phytophthora infestation, often indicated by areas of lesser primocane emergence as well as floricane dieback, begins in patches and seems to spread over time (fig. 5.8).

Affected plants show weak lateral branches and leaves, which become yellow and dry out at the margins and between the leaf veins. As the infestation increases in severity, affected plants will wilt and die, especially as weather turns warmer and fruits begin to form and fill. Roots from Phytophthora-infested but not yet dead plants will appear reddish brown just beneath the epidermis, rather than the white of healthy root tissue. This is only a preliminary indicator, and confirmations of Phytophthora infestation should be done at a diagnostic laboratory for plant diseases.

Since Phytophthora thrives in wet areas, it can be mitigated by planting caneberries into well-drained soils on beds raised at least 8 inches high. Proper irrigation management, based on plant needs and weather conditions, is also important in creating situations where excessive moisture does not become conducive to pathogen activity and growth.

Red raspberries are the most susceptible to Phytophthora, while black raspberries and blackberries seem to be relatively resistant to this disease, although they can suffer if planted in very wet areas. Within the red raspberries, varieties exist that are fairly tolerant of the disease, such as Latham, Boyne, Killarney, Caroline, and Nordic. On the other hand, Titan, Ruby, Heritage, and Polana are quite susceptible.

Fumigation is an effective way to reduce the amount of Phytophthora present in a field prior to planting. Although the use of methyl bromide is substantially restricted, several alternative fumigants are available for use in caneberries. Two formulations of 1,3-D and chloropicrin are labeled for preplant fumigation of soils.

Along with a drip-tape-applied fungicide, there are several pesticides, including registered and effective fungicides containing phosphorous acid, with efficacy on Phytophthora. Users of the above fungicides should be aware of relatively long preharvest intervals when using these materials.

Figure 5.8. Area of raspberry field affected by Phytophthora root rot. *Photo:* Mark Bolda.

Verticillium Wilt

The species of *Verticillium* that causes Verticillium wilt is a soil pathogen that has a broad host range, including strawberries, tomatoes, potatoes, peppers, squash, melons, stone fruits, and many weed species. While not nearly as common in California caneberries as Phytophthora, Verticillium wilt can be severe on black raspberries and boysenberries and on red raspberries and loganberries. Blackberries vary in their susceptibility to this disease.

In hot weather, leaves on new canes of Verticillium-affected plants become yellow and may drop off. In contrast to Phytophthora root rot, Verticillium wilt symptoms start at the bottom of the cane and move up it; in some cases only one side of the cane or plant may be affected. Cooler weather may leave the impression that the plants are recovering, since severity of wilting appears to decrease.

The symptoms above are only preliminary indicators, and growers who suspect infestation from *Verticillium* should submit samples to a diagnostic laboratory. Additionally, growers who suspect that a field is infested with *Verticillium* should take soil samples prior to selecting that field for planting of susceptible varieties.

As with Phytophthora, fumigation is an effective way to reduce the amount of *Verticillium* present in a field prior to planting. For situations where fumigation is not a possibility and the summer fallow period is warm enough (for example, the Central Valley in California), growers can use soil solarization. Rotation away from disease hosts for at least 4 years is one way to reduce problems with *Verticillium* wilt. However, the wide host range of *Verticillium* makes it difficult to rotate away from susceptible hosts for several years. Popular nonhost plants are broccoli, cauliflower, and, sudangrass.

Use of clean planting stock is highly recommended, which also helps avoid introducing this disease into areas that are free of it.

Foliar and Fruit Diseases

Leaf Spot

Leaf spot on blackberries is caused by *Mycosphaerella rubi* and is very similar in symptoms and control measures to the less common leaf spot, caused by *Sphaerulina rubi*, on red raspberry.

Leaf spot appears on the leaves as roughly circular lesions that have a purple margin and a very small, lightly colored center. Once the lesion is mature, the light-colored center often displays small, globose, black fungal fruiting bodies known as pycnidia. These lesions also occur on blackberry canes and petioles, although they are a little more elongate than circular in shape.

The leaf spot pathogen is usually first brought into the field on contaminated nursery stock. Once introduced, it is spread by wind and splashing water. Periods of high humidity and rain are very advantageous for the spread of this disease. *M. rubi* spends the winter mostly as mycelium and pycnidia in dead leaves and caneberry stems.

Blackberry hedgerow management is key in the control of leaf spot. Practices that improve air circulation in the hedgerow, such as proper in-row spacing, pruning, and the removal of fruited canes and dead leaves, are all recommended. Covering the crop with macro-tunnels gives excellent reduction of leaf spot disease potential. Purchase of clean nursery stock is an important step in reducing the entrance of this disease into the field in the first place.

In addition, applications of lime sulfur as a dormant spray and copper sulfate late in the season are helpful in managing leaf spot. Fungicides effective for Botrytis also have efficacy for leaf spot.

Cladosporium Fruit Rot

Cladosporium fruit rot occurs on all types of caneberries and is caused by two species of *Cladosporium* fungus. Cladosporium does not generally harm the fruit, and removal of the fungus from the fruit will reveal very little damage to the tissues underneath. Nevertheless, the dark to olive green fungal growth on fruit is unsightly and leaves the fruit unmarketable. Cladosporium is known as a postharvest pathogen, but it also occurs in the field, especially in moist areas with little air circulation.

Cladosporium fruit rot can be controlled by methods that maintain proper air circulation and dryness of the caneberry hedgerow, such as proper in-row spacing, trellising, removal of fruited canes, and coverage with macro-tunnels. Regular harvest and removal of overripe and damaged fruit, as well as timely cooling of harvested fruit, are also essential to limiting the advance of this disease.

Powdery Mildew

Powdery mildew is caused by the pathogen *Sphaerotheca macularis* and is found in red, black, and purple raspberries, along with blackberries (fig. 5.9).

Plants affected by powdery mildew show a range of symptoms, initially visible as light green spots on upper leaf surfaces and white, powdery growth directly underneath. The white fungal growth tends to be found first on young leaves, especially those at the tips of primocanes. Canes heavily infested by powdery mildew may appear long and spindly, with leaves smaller than normal. Heavily infested plants will be stunted and produce significantly less fruit.

Powdery mildew overwinters in infected buds of canes, and when shoots grow out from these buds, they become infected as well. Since the fungus produces spores, the disease can easily spread by air currents. Disease development is most rapid in periods of warm weather (between 50° and 70°F) accompanied by high relative humidity and dry leaf surfaces.

Removal of affected primocanes and pruning of floricanes can be useful in reducing the amount of inoculum of powdery mildew available for further infestations.

Along with several registered fungicides, flowable sulfur, potassium bicarbonate, and certain horticultural oils are registered for use in controlling powdery mildew in caneberries.

Downy Mildew

On occasion in California there have been outbreaks of the disease of downy mildew on caneberries. Downy mildew is most prevalent in California in the spring and fall in periods of high moisture (rainfall) and temperatures of 64° to 71°F. Downy mildew is most serious on boysenberries, blackberry-red raspberry hybrids, and certain varieties of blackberries.

Downy mildew affects the leaves, petioles, primocanes, pedicels, calyces, and fruit of susceptible varieties, and it can become systemic in the most susceptible varieties under ideal conditions (fig. 5.10).

Downy mildew is caused by the fungal pathogen *Peronospora sparsa*. The disease first appears as a yellow discoloration on the upper leaf surface, followed by a red to purple discoloration. This discoloration often takes on an angular appearance, since it is framed and limited by veins of the leaf. These blotches appear as light pink or tan areas on the leaf underside, often accompanied by whitish spore masses easily visible with a dissecting microscope. As favorable wet and moderately warm conditions persist and the disease advances, these lesions expand to cover the whole leaf, and eventually the whole leaf turns brown and may even fall off the plant if the disease is severe.

Infested flowers often result in fruit that is crumbly and not sound, while green fruit infested with downy mildew will shrivel and dry out. Fruit infested at the mature stage takes on a dull pallor, followed by the fruit shriveling and drying out. Some infested fruit will split into two parts.

Figure 5.9. Powdery mildew on blackberry primocane. *Photo:* Mark Bolda.

Figure 5.10. Downy mildew on blackberry leaf. *Photo:* Steven Koike.

Clean planting stock should be used as an initial measure for mitigation of downy mildew. Fields destined for caneberry production should have histories clear of caneberry downy mildew infestation, as well as being clear of the alternate hosts for downy mildew such as wild blackberry and rose. Removal of old fruited canes has a large role in reducing an important inoculum source of downy mildew.

Downy mildew and other diseases thrive in moist conditions, and plants should be pruned and trained to maintain air circulation in the hedgerow and to promote light penetration in the lower canopy. The row and inter-row should not be overgrown with weeds and caneberry suckers. Additionally, the use of macro-tunnels over the crop greatly reduces the potential for downy mildew infestation.

As with Phytophthora, phosphorous acid containing pesticides can be useful in managing infestations of downy mildew. Please refer to that section for further information.

Rust on Caneberries

Rusts are important pathogens of caneberries grown in the Monterey Bay region of the Central Coast. Caneberry rusts appear as yellow, orange, or rust-colored dusty pustules on leaves, canes, and occasionally flowers and fruit. Effects on the plant can range from very little damage and minor leaf spots to leaf death, defoliation, and significant reduction of marketable fruit yield. Rust fungi have perhaps the most complex life cycles of any plant pathogen group. The rusts usually form distinct spore stages that may infect different parts of the host plant and have different appearances and colors. The life cycles of these fungi are further complicated by the fact that some rust species have their various spore stages infecting different hosts. Typical spore stages are the following: aeciospores (usually occurring early in the season and produced in structures called aecia), urediniospores (occurring midseason and produced in uredinia), and teliospores (occurring late in the season and produced in telia).

It is important for growers to be aware that there are several species of rust infecting caneberries in this area, and that the potential for damage and control measures may vary according to the rust specie. Each caneberry rust is often specific to a certain caneberry type, be it red raspberry, black raspberry, purple raspberry, or blackberry. If growers want to be absolutely certain which rust is infecting their crop, they should contact their local cooperative extension office for help in identification.

Yellow rust

Yellow rust is caused by the pathogen *Phragmidium rubi-idaei*. Of the major caneberry crops, only red raspberry is susceptible to infection, and it is not a systemic pathogen, meaning that the pathogen does not spread internally through the plant. In the spring, one sees the yellowish orange aecia forming only on the tops of raspberry leaves and on foliage that is closer to the ground (fig. 5.11). Aecia occurring early on the tops of the leaves is a general sign that distinguishes this rust from late leaf rust, which also infects red raspberry. Severely affected leaves can dry out and die. Later, in June and July, one will see orange to yellow uredinia on the undersides of leaves; these structures later darken as black teliospores develop from the middle of July to the fall. The yellow rust fungus overwinters as teliospores on the bark of remaining floricanes (fruiting canes). Such canes are the sources of inoculum that affect emerging leaves and primocanes (vegetative canes) the following spring.

If possible, completely remove the floricanes and first flush of primocanes. This is useful in controlling this disease, as it removes most sources of inoculum. Furthermore, any method of pruning that improves air circulation is helpful in reducing yellow rust, as this allows leaves, flowers, and fruit to dry more quickly, subsequently reducing plant susceptibility. There are several fungicides labeled for use in caneberries that control yellow rust.

Figure 5.11. Yellow rust on leaves of red raspberry. *Photo:* Mark Bolda.

Late leaf rust

Late leaf rust is caused by the pathogen *Pucci-niastrum americanum.* It infects red and purple raspberry and is not a systemic pathogen. As the name *late leaf rust* suggests, later in the season (beginning in July) many small spots of this rust are found on the older, lower leaves of raspberries. These spots first turn yellow and then brown. In severe cases plants can be defoliated, and the rust can also infect flowers and fruit. Yellow uredinia and powdery urediniospores form on the bottom sides of leaves. In the fall, telia and teliospores appear as brown growth within existing uredinia.

Since this pathogen's alternate host, white spruce *(Picea glauca),* is not common in the coastal areas of California, the fungus probably overwinters as mycelium within remaining canes and produces urediniospores in the spring. These spring uredin-iospores then infect the growing plants. Spores of *P. americanum* are spread by wind, and infection of leaves is favored by high relative humidity.

As with yellow rust, any method that improves air circulation in the raspberry hedgerow is helpful in mitigating the spread and development of this disease. Also, the removal of infected floricanes and primocanes is useful in that it takes away an important source of inoculum. Several fungicides are effective in the control of late leaf rust. Growers should also know that some red raspberry varieties are resistant to the disease, including the popular Nova floricane-bearing variety.

Cane and leaf rust

Cane and leaf rust can be found on some of the blackberry cultivars grown in coastal areas. This rust is not systemic but can be damaging in that it can cause plant stress and some defoliation. Normally, cane and leaf rust does not infect the fruit, although masses of spores falling on the fruit can render it unmarketable anyway. This disease is rarely found on raspberry.

Cane and leaf rust is caused by the pathogen *Kuehneola uredinis.* This rust appears as bright yellow spore masses (uredinia) in splits and cracks in the bark of stems and on the undersides of leaves (fig. 5.12). In the fall, the brown teliospore stage develops within uredinia. It is important not to confuse this common blackberry disease with the less common but far more damaging orange rust (see below for description).

For control, remove old, diseased canes after fruiting. A spray control program is recommended, consisting of winter applications of lime sulfur followed by fixed copper sprays, applied once at green tip stage and then at bloom. Cane and leaf rust is controlled by several fungicides registered for use on caneberries.

Orange rust

The damaging orange rust disease is occasionally observed in the Monterey Bay caneberry-growing area of California. It is important for growers to be aware of it, so that timely control measures can be taken to prevent its further spread if it is discovered.

Orange rust is caused by two pathogens, *Arthu-riomyces peckianus* and *Gymnoconia nitens.* These fungi are distinguished from each other by differences in spore appearance and by whether they have a long *(Arthuriomyces)* or short *(Gymnoconia)* life cycle. This disease can be found on blackberries and on black raspberries. Orange rust is systemic, and it therefore grows into plant crowns and roots and remains in the plant for life. Although this pathogen is not known to kill plants outright, it weakens them severely, and systemically infected plants produce few or no blossoms.

Newly emerging leaves of infected plants appear stunted, deformed, and yellowish. From afar, the plant tends to have a lightly foliated, spindly appearance. Later, the undersides of diseased leaves

Figure 5.12. Cane and leaf rust *(Kuehneola uredinis)* in trailing blackberry. *Photo:* Mark Bolda.

will exhibit irregularly shaped, waxy orange aecia, which soon turn to a powdery bright orange as they rupture and release spores (fig. 5.13). Late in the season, brown-black pustules of the teliospore stage will develop on lower leaf surfaces. A notable symptom is the growth of many small, typically weak shoots from the base of the plant; such shoots are usually not productive.

Diseased plants, once confirmed to be infected with orange rust, should be promptly uprooted, removed from the field, and destroyed. This roguing should be done before the production and release of spores. Although this control measure may seem severe, it must be done in order to prevent the further spread of orange rust.

There are varieties of blackberry resistant to orange rust. The Arkansas series of erect blackberries (Choctaw, Apache, Navajo, Chickasaw) as well as Eldorado, Raven, Snyder, and Ebony King are reported to be resistant to this disease.

The best control measure for orange rust is prevention—starting out with clean plant stock obtained from a quality, reputable plant nursery.

Botrytis Gray Mold

Caused by the pathogen *Botrytis cinerea,* Botrytis gray mold is a common disease of caneberries, especially in red raspberries. The most common symptom of Botrytis infection is a gray, brown, or tan powdery growth on ripening or ripe fruit (fig. 5.14). Rarely, this growth may be seen on the flowers. Botrytis is a serious postharvest pathogen, as rotted or infested but symptom-free fruit will contaminate healthy fruit in shipping containers.

Botrytis survives the winter on plant residue as hard, darkened masses of fungal hyphae called sclerotia. Botrytis spores then spread to flowers by air circulation and splashing from rain and irrigation, especially under cool and wet conditions. This primary infestation of the flower is latent until the fruit is nearly ripe or ripe, at which point it manifests in the gray to brown powdery symptom described above. Some infestation is direct onto mature fruit, but this is not considered to be as important as the infestation of flowers.

Another important disease caused by *Botrytis* is the infestation of canes known as cane Botrytis. While varying in severity, it has been known to kill the cane in some varieties. The most obvious symptoms of cane Botrytis are the banding or watermark lines radiating out from a spur on the cane in a concentric ring pattern. Tissue underneath an affected cane will appear to be healthy. During periods of high moisture, sclerotia formed beneath the epidermis of the cane may grow out to the gray to brown powdery growth seen on the fruit.

Best management of Botrytis gray mold is achieved through an integrated approach. Since the

Figure 5.13. Orange rust infesting blackberry. *Photo:* Mark Bolda.

Figure 5.14. Blackberry fruit infested with Botrytis. *Photo:* Mark Bolda.

pathogen favors moisture, steps taken to reduce the amount of moisture, such as proper pruning and trellising of the hedgerow, as well as the use of macro-tunnels to cover the crop, reduce the incidence of this disease. In the case of cane Botrytis, removal of the first flush of primocanes has been shown to reduce the severity of cane Botrytis. Timely removal of overripe fruit can reduce the potential for buildup of inoculum of *Botrytis*. While there are several fungicides registered for use in conventionally grown caneberries, they will be less effective in the absence of other cultural control measures.

Bacterial Diseases

Crown Gall

Crown gall is caused by *Agrobacterium tumefaciens* and appears as a spongy to hard, tumorlike growth of up to an inch in diameter on the crown or roots of the caneberry plant (fig. 5.15). It occurs on red, purple, and black raspberries and blackberries.

The crown gall bacterium enters the plant through a wound. Once *Agrobacterium tumefaciens* enters the plant, it causes nearby cells to multiply and enlarge, resulting in the misshaping of caneberry tissue into what is called a gall. The enlarging and multiplying of plant cells can interfere with the movement of water and nutrients through the plant, and it can cause injury based on the extent of growth in the plant. Severely affected plants can be stunted and bear small and seedy fruit.

Crown gall may be prevented by avoiding injury in those areas most susceptible to infestation—namely, the crown and roots of the plant. Clean nursery stock and rotation to nonsusceptible hosts such as strawberry, grains, pasture, or most vegetables for a period of 2 years or more are also viable options. Fumigation is not an effective control measure.

The biological control agent *Agrobacterium radiobacter* strain K-84 is available for use in crown gall control. It is applied to roots of caneberries when planting, with the intention of protecting the roots of the developing plant from infection. *Agrobacterium radiobacter* strain K-84 is only a preventative measure and will not cure an infected plant.

Viruses

Viruses are systemic and can be found all through the vegetative portions of the plant. Once a plant is infected with viruses, it cannot be cured; so growers should know that the key to virus control is prevention through the acquisition of clean plant stock.

It is important to know that virus infestation manifests itself differently on different varieties of the caneberry type known to be hosts. The symptom descriptions below should thus be considered only a basic guide to identification. To obtain a definitive identification of a virus, it is strongly recommended that growers submit a sample to a plant disease diagnostic laboratory.

Figure 5.15. Crown gall on Triple Crown blackberry. *Photo:* Mark Bolda.

Raspberry Bushy Dwarf Virus (RBDV)

Raspberry bushy dwarf infects many varieties of red raspberry and black raspberry. RBDV can lead to significant loss in vigor and yield in raspberries. RBDV is spread by pollen and causes abortion of drupelets, leading to a crumbly fruit. In some varieties, such as Autumn Bliss and Caroline, it also causes an interveinal chlorosis, leaving parts of the plant yellow. Infections of RBDV mixed with other viruses can cause more severe damage than single infections.

Although RBDV is spread by pollen from infected plants through the activities of pollinating insects, and deflowered plants have been shown to resist infection when near infected plants, restriction of pollination is not practical in most cases. Control of RBDV is limited to obtaining certified, virus-free plant stock from a nursery and using immune varieties. The varieties Willamette, Haida, Heritage, and Latham are immune to common RBDV isolates in North America.

Tomato Ringspot Virus (TomRSV)

A widely distributed virus occurring in red raspberry and occasionally blackberry and black raspberry in North America is tomato ringspot virus (TomRSV). TomRSV occurs on many crops and weeds, such as dandelion, chickweed, fruit trees, grapes, strawberries, blueberries, and others. Damage caused by TomRSV can range from none to crumbly fruit to weakening of the plant and death.

TomRSV can cause large losses in red raspberry plantations. Symptoms of infestation can be yellow rings or systems of thin yellow lines on the leaves on first-year plantings. These symptoms are then not really seen in following years, although affected areas will show stunting and fruit that are smaller than normal and crumbly.

TomRSV is spread by the dagger nematode *(Xiphinema americanum)* from infested nursery stock or infested plants around the field. The disease will spread through a field at a rate of around 6 feet per year.

Control of TomRSV is done by prevention and by removal of recognizably infested plants. Obtaining only virus-free transplants for planting and preplant fumigating for nematode control are both important steps in preventing this virus from entering the field. If affected plants are discovered, they should be removed, along with surrounding weeds, suckers, and raspberry plants. It is recommended to remove plants up to five plants away on either side of the affected plant, as these may be infested while not yet showing symptoms.

Disorders Caused by Abiotic Factors

Crumbly Fruit

There are several possible causes of crumbly fruit in caneberries.

Poor pollination. Extreme weather conditions, either hot or cold, affect pollination and can also cause crumbly fruit. Honeybees do not move very well, if at all, in extremities of weather, and this can result in uneven pollination, meaning that some drupelets will not be fully formed and will result in a crumbly fruit.

The pattern of crumbly fruit may be useful in indicating the cause. Viruses infest the whole plant, and an infested plant would have crumbly fruit up and down the cane. Extremities in weather most often occur over a few days, so only those flowers exposed to these conditions will express crumbliness. Crumbly fruit then would be found through the whole field only at a certain height of cane in the case of exposure to poor weather.

Poor propagation. If not properly done, plant propagation can transport problems initially found only on a few plants to large numbers of nursery stock. It is important that growers always work with and purchase only plant stock that is certified.

Glyphosate injury. Glyphosate (Roundup) is occasionally used for weed control between hedgerows of caneberries. Since it is translocatable, it can be transported from any part of the plant (e.g., caneberry suckers) to another part, such as the parent plant. Symptoms of injury can take weeks to develop, especially when weather is cloudy and cool. Symptoms of injury are small yellow leaves at the growing points that do not fully expand. Glyphosate can be most damaging in the fall or late summer, when the caneberry plant is translocating material downward into the root system.

Paraquat injury. Paraquat is more commonly used than glyphosate for weed control and sucker burnback in caneberries. It is a nonselective herbicide with contact action within 24 hours, but it does not move within the plant as glyphosate does. In early spring, the epidermis of lower canes is not damaged by paraquat, but any contact of leaves by the spray will result in rapid browning, upward curling, and desiccation of the leaves. Light (as in clear, sunny days) accelerates the development of symptoms.

Sunscald. Clear days accompanied by high temperatures (> 90° F) can result in sunscald of caneberry fruit, especially in the darker-colored blackberries. Caroline red raspberry also seems to be particularly susceptible. Fruit not covered by plant foliage will become light brown to white on the drupelets directly facing the sun (fig. 5.16).

Frost. Frost injury to caneberries in California, unlike the cold injury experienced in other parts of the United States, tends not to kill the canes, and least of all the floricanes. Frost injury in California is mostly limited to injury of the flowers of early fruiting varieties (such as Nova or Prelude) due to late spring frosts taking place in April. The result of frost to caneberry flowers is necrosis on all of the internal organs of the flower, causing no fruit to be produced there. Flowers emerging before or after the frost are fine and fruit normally.

Weeds

As in other crops, control of weeds in caneberries is important. Excessive weeds retain moisture in the lower canopy, to the detriment of fruit quality, and they harbor unwanted pests. Once established, however, both raspberries and blackberries can be quite vigorous and can compete with weed growth in the row to some extent, but some selective weeding will always be necessary.

Control of weeds in the first year depends on the quality of site preparation. Fumigation eliminates most weed species (except hard-coated species that resist fumigant penetration and those dispersed by air after fumigation), and a properly maintained site prior to planting can also reduce the amount of weeds in the first year of a caneberry plantation.

It is imperative to eliminate weeds prior to seed production. Cultivation is an important weed control measure. When cultivating early in the development of a new planting, soil should be thrown into the row to smother small weeds. Within the row, weeds can be hand-hoed early in the season as long as the hedgerow has not filled in too much. Once the hedgerow has filled in, the canopy should be shaded enough to reduce the number of weeds emerging, thus minimizing the amount of effort required to keep this area clear of weeds.

Mowing the areas between the rows to control weeds or cane suckers is also an alternative. Weeds can be mowed with or without a perennial crop established in the area between the rows. Repeated mowing weakens weeds and keeps them from competing with the plants or interfering with harvest or other field operations.

Herbicides registered for use in caneberries can be useful in weed control as well as in primocane suppression. Contact herbicides that are not translocated can be used to eliminate weeds and early primocane shoots in the spring. Note, however, that these herbicides are not very useful in controlling perennial weeds, since they kill only the foliage and not the crowns and roots. Postemergent grass herbicides will work on most grasses if applied when the grasses are less than 6 inches tall.

Figure 5.16. White druplet on Apache blackberry. *Photo:* Mark Bolda.

Growers should recognize that different caneberry cultivars respond differently to herbicides, so care should always be taken with their use. Always read and follow herbicide labels carefully.

Mulching is occasionally recommended for caneberries to aid weed control. Mulching may offer other advantages as well, such as moderation of soil temperatures and moisture retention. Mulching has traditionally been little used in California because growers have not consistently seen that the benefits outweigh the additional costs. Most California caneberry plantings are relatively short term (1.5 to 3 years), and mulching may not be justified in these circumstances. Mulch application may be more justified in smaller-scale or longer-cycle plantings, particularly in inland areas where soil temperature and moisture consistency are more of a problem than in coastal areas.

6 Irrigation, Water Quality, and Fertility

Caneberries need adequate soil moisture to promote cane growth and continuous flowering, as well as to maximize fruit yield and quality. Caneberries grown in most regions of California require supplemental irrigation to meet the seasonal water needs of the crop, especially during low-rainfall months in the summer and fall or when grown in covered tunnels.

Irrigation Methods for Caneberries

Sprinkler

Overhead sprinklers are used in California mainly to establish transplants. Subsequently, drip irrigation is used after trellises are installed and leaves have emerged. Sprinklers can also provide protection against frost during the winter and early spring; during the summer, they can provide protection from excessive heat, which may cause flowers to abort. However, these uses of sprinklers are rare in coastal regions, where much of the commercial caneberry production is located. Sprinklers are rarely used to irrigate a crop for the entire season, since prolonged moisture on foliage and fruit promotes diseases and reduces fruit quality. Also, wet conditions between rows promote weeds and may interfere with harvesting and other field operations such as spraying and fertilizing. Under some circumstances, sprinklers are used to supplement drip irrigations. Sprinklers may be used to rewet the soil profile when soil moisture is restricted to a narrow zone around the drip tape. Sprinklers may also be used to leach salts that accumulate near the soil surface.

Furrow

Furrow irrigation is not commonly used for caneberry production in California. However, furrow irrigation may be practical for establishing new plantings if sprinklers are not available. Plants should be grown on berms or beds to prevent waterlogging and the promotion of fungal diseases in roots and crowns. Furrow irrigation is best suited to fields prepared with a consistent and gradual slope (less than 0.5 percent) and on medium-textured, deep soils. As in the case of sprinklers, furrow irrigation may interfere with field operations such as harvesting and cultivation.

Drip

Drip irrigation is commonly used to water caneberries after the crop has been established. Drip lines may be placed on the soil surface next to the plant rows until trellises are installed. After trellises are set up, the drip lines are usually attached to a guide wire approximately 12 to 18 inches above the soil surface. Subsurface (buried) drip is not often used for caneberries because accessing the tape or hose for repairs is more difficult than with surface or above-surface drip. Subsurface drip tape could be useful for thorny varieties, which can puncture tape; however, using thick-walled drip hose is also an effective strategy to prevent punctures. Subsurface drip may be more effective than surface drip at reducing weed competition and evaporation losses by keeping the soil surface dry.

The application (distribution) uniformity of a well-designed drip system is often above 85 percent, depending on the system design, the terrain, and how well the system is operated and maintained. Selection of appropriate drip components is critical to designing a system with high application uniformity. Irrigation system designers can help growers achieve the most cost-effective solutions for their growing conditions. Designs should take into consideration the water source and pumping capacity, potential pressure fluctuations, field dimensions, and elevation changes. Proper filtration of water is necessary to prevent clogging of emitters and maintain high distribution uniformity. Additionally, the drip lines should be periodically flushed, especially if fertilizers are delivered through the irrigation system. Typical components of drip systems include backflow prevention, vacuum and air release valves, filter station, pressure gauge, pressure regulator, flow meter, main and submain pipes, and drip tape or drip hoses.

Drip has many advantages over sprinkler and furrow irrigation. By not wetting the soil between plant rows, drip reduces evaporation losses and can reduce weed competition as well as increase the accessibility of the field to equipment and harvest crews. Drip irrigation reduces runoff, which can occur with sprinkler and furrow irrigation, and drip irrigation systems can be designed for fields with steep slopes. By not wetting foliage and fruit, drip irrigation reduces risks for fungal and bacterial diseases. Because drip systems apply water at a lower rate than sprinkler and furrow irrigation, a larger area can be irrigated at the same time. The lower pressures needed for drip compared to sprinklers may reduce pumping costs. Growers usually have the most control of soil moisture using drip technology because irrigations can be frequent without interfering with harvest and field operations. Fertilizers (and some pesticides) can be delivered to the crop through the drip system, providing a method to apply small but frequent doses of fertilizer to match the nutrient demand of the crop. This strategy of fertilizing (fertigation) can increase nutrient-use efficiency and provide an opportunity to reduce leaching of nitrate, which can contaminate groundwater supplies.

Although drip has many advantages over sprinkler and furrow irrigation, it is the most expensive irrigation method. Initial costs for drip range between $1,000 and $1,700 per acre, depending on the choice of tape, filters, and main and submain materials. In order to take advantage of the ability to irrigate and fertigate frequently with drip, more management is required than with sprinklers and furrow. Because water is applied slowly with drip, more time is needed for irrigating than with

sprinklers and furrow. Another potential disadvantage of drip irrigation is that the roots become confined to a zone defined by the wetting pattern of the drip system. During periods of high water use, this zone can become very limited if irrigations do not adequately keep up with the water use of the crop. This potential problem can be resolved with proper irrigation scheduling, but it can be more problematic on soil types that have restricted lateral movement of moisture, such as sandy soils or clay-textured soils that crack when dry.

Water Needs

The majority of the water used by caneberries is transpired through the leaves. Additionally, some moisture is lost by evaporation from the soil surface and through percolation below the root zone. Only a small fraction of the water taken up by the crop is stored in fruits and removed at harvest. Field studies on the Central Coast have demonstrated that the water use of raspberries varies between 8 and 18 inches per crop, depending on weather conditions and when the crop is planted and harvested. For example, first-year primocane crops planted in December and harvested during the fall of the following year required 17 inches of water. In contrast, second-year floricane crops needed less than 8 inches of water, since they were irrigated only during the spring and early summer months. Water use can be as low as 0.02 inches per day during winter months or foggy days and as high as 0.25 inches per day during summer months. The shade from macro-tunnels reduces water use by 20 to 30 percent compared to crops in open-field conditions.

Most growers try to maintain soil moisture between upper and lower thresholds to avoid overstressing the crop and to prevent oversaturation in the root zone. Water stress can reduce pollination, cause fruit to abort, and reduce fruit size. Water stress can also affect fruiting during the subsequent season. For example, in a study conducted on the Central Coast of California, a water deficit sufficient to cause yield loss in the first-year primocane crop also induced yield loss in the second-year floricane crop, though the second season crop was adequately watered.

Wet soil conditions lead to an anaerobic environment and can promote fungal diseases that cause root rot. Saturated conditions also create excessive drainage, which carries mobile nutrients such as nitrate below the root zone. To maintain soil moisture at optimal levels, the crop needs to be irrigated uniformly and irrigations should be scheduled to match the water consumption rate of the crop.

Irrigation Scheduling

Irrigation scheduling involves deciding when and how much to irrigate for optimizing production and quality. Irrigation schedules are calculated from information about the crop, soil, irrigation system, and water source. The minimal information needed to develop an irrigation schedule is 1) the amount of water the crop needs, 2) the rate that the irrigation system supplies water to the crop, and 3) the water-holding capacity of the soil. Although the calculations are simple, a worksheet or spreadsheet is often helpful for developing and keeping track of an irrigation schedule. Finally, simple tools—such as a flow meter to measure how much water is applied and instruments for monitoring soil moisture levels—can be used to verify that the watering schedule is correct.

Weather-Based Scheduling

Weather-based approaches to scheduling irrigations are used for many cultivated crops. Wind speed, air temperature, relative humidity, and solar radiation affect plant water use or, more specifically, the water lost by evaporation from the soil and by transpiration from the leaves of the crop. Using evapotranspiration (ET) data (evaporation + transpiration) from the California Irrigation Management Information System (CIMIS), the consumptive water use of a crop (in units of inches or mm per day) can be estimated. CIMIS ET data is available from the Department of Water Resources website (www.cimis.water.ca.gov) for more than 120 locations in California. It is generated by weather stations located on irrigated grass, which serves as a reference crop. Historical, biweekly average reference (grass) ET values for two locations on the Central Coast of California are presented in table 6.1.

Table 6.1. Average crop water use (ET) of grass measured at the South Salinas and Pajaro CIMIS weather stations, 1995–2002

South Salinas			Pajaro		
Month	Day	Reference crop ET (inch/day)	Month	Day	Reference crop ET (inch/day)
Jan	1–15	0.04	Jan	1–15	0.05
	16–31	0.05		16–31	0.04
Feb	1–15	0.06	Feb	1–15	0.06
	16–28	0.07		16–28	0.07
Mar	1–15	0.09	Mar	1–15	0.09
	16–31	0.12		16–31	0.12
Apr	1–15	0.14	Apr	1–15	0.13
	16–30	0.17		16–30	0.17
May	1–15	0.17	May	1–15	0.17
	16–31	0.18		16–31	0.17
June	1–15	0.21	June	1–15	0.18
	16–30	0.22		16–30	0.18
July	1–15	0.21	July	1–15	0.17
	16–31	0.19		16–31	0.15
Aug	1–15	0.19	Aug	1–15	0.16
	16–31	0.18		16–31	0.14
Sept	1–15	0.16	Sept	1–15	0.14
	16–30	0.13		16–30	0.11
Oct	1–15	0.12	Oct	1–15	0.11
	16–31	0.09		16–31	0.08
Nov	1–15	0.07	Nov	1–15	0.06
	16–30	0.05		16–30	0.05
Dec	1–15	0.04	Dec	1–15	0.04
	16–31	0.05		16–31	0.05

ET can be estimated for a specific crop by multiplying reference ET data and the appropriate crop coefficient (Kc):

$$ET_{crop} = ET_{ref} \times Kc$$

The value of Kc can range from 0.1 to 1.1 and is closely related to the percentage of ground shaded by the canopy. Irrigation method and physiological stages, such as flowering and senescence, are also factored into the crop coefficient. Crop ET values should be adjusted down by 20 to 30 percent for berries grown under macro-tunnels. Because crop coefficients are not available for caneberries, estimates of canopy cover serve as a close substitute for the Kc values using a modified version of the above equation.

$$ET_{crop} = ET_{ref} \times (\% \text{ canopy cover} \div 100)$$

For example, if raspberry canopy covers about 75 percent of the soil surface in June, and the CIMIS reference ET was 0.18 inches per day, the crop would require:

$$0.18 \text{ inch/day} \times (75 \div 100) = 0.135 \text{ inch/day}$$

However, due to the upright stature of caneberry crops, canopy cover can be difficult to estimate. Overhead photos of the crop can be useful for approximating canopy cover. Figure 6.1 shows views of a raspberry canopy from above the row and from the end of the row at various stages of development. Table 6.2 presents canopy cover estimates for a primocane raspberry variety planted in December on the Central Coast.

By irrigating enough to replace water lost by evapotranspiration, it is possible to optimize irrigations for production and minimize percolation below the root zone. Also, it is possible to avoid under-irrigating during periods of high water consumption, which can result in stress and reduced growth.

Rooting Pattern

Irrigation schedules need to consider the rooting pattern of the crop. A new planting, with shallow roots, will require frequent irrigations because of its limited access to soil moisture compared with a mature crop with deep roots, which can penetrate into subsoil moisture. Caneberry root systems reach depths of 3 feet in a uniform, well-drained soil (figs. 6.2 and 6.3).

An impeding layer, such as a hardpan, clay layer, or perched water table, can limit the rooting depth and the roots' ability to extract available moisture from the lower profile. Approximately 90 percent of the roots may be located in the upper 18 inches of the soil (see fig. 6.2). The extent of horizontal root growth depends on tillage practices employed between the rows and irrigation method used. Periodic chiseling or disking between rows may prune roots near the soil surface. Overhead sprinklers encourage lateral growth of roots because the soil is moistened between the plant rows. As mentioned before, drip irrigation can confine roots to a narrow zone of moisture centered on the plant row.

Soil Water-Holding Capacity

Each soil has a unique composition of sand-, silt-, and clay-sized particles, which gives the soil its texture and also determines the amount of water that a soil can hold. Fine-textured soils, with high amounts of clay, hold more water than coarse or medium-textured soils with high amounts of silt and sand. A coarse soil will usually need to be irrigated more frequently but for less time than a fine- or medium-textured soil. The amount of water held in soil is usually compared in units of inches of water per foot depth of soil. Available water is the difference between the amount of water stored in the soil at field capacity and at wilting point.

Table 6.2. Average canopy cover for first-year primocane raspberries

Fall crop, first-year canes	
Days after leaf budbreak*	Canopy cover (%)
67	12
77	16
87	22
97	30
107	38
117	48
127	58
137	67
147	75
157	82
167	87

Note: *Leaf budbreak was estimated to occur Feb. 15 for a Dec. 5 planting date.

Figure 6.1. Canopy cover of first-year primocane raspberry as viewed from the end of a row and from 14 feet aboveground using an infrared camera: 7% (A, B), 18% (C, D), and 34% (E, F) ground cover. *Photos:* Michael Cahn.

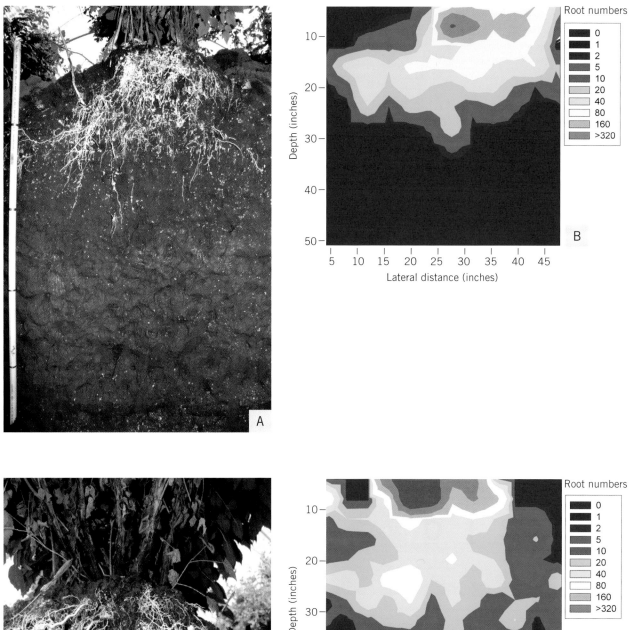

Figure 6.2. Cross-section view of root distribution of first-year (A, B) and second-year (C, D) primocane raspberry. Roots were spray painted white to enhance contrast in photos. Units are root number per 15.6 square inches. *Photos:* Michael Cahn.

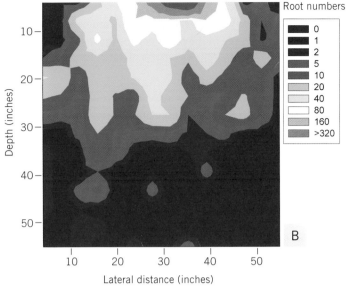

Figure 6.3. Cross-section view of root distribution of second-year blackberry (A, B). Roots were spray painted white to enhance contrast in photos. Units are root number per 15.6 square inches. *Photos:* Michael Cahn.

Table 6.3 estimates available water in soil for a range of textures. For example, the available water stored in 3 feet of a loam soil would be 5.4 inches:

Total available water = 1.8 inches/foot × 3 feet = 5.4 inches

For caneberries, the total available moisture stored in the soil profile should not be depleted beyond 20 to 30 percent before the next irrigation. For the above example, if the water use of a crop with roots extending to a 3-foot depth is 0.18 inches per day, the irrigation interval would be:

5.4 inches × 20% ÷ 0.18 inches/day = 6 days

The amount of water applied would be:

6 days × 0.18 inches/day = 1.1 inches

Soil Moisture Monitoring

Monitoring of soil moisture is recommended to check that irrigations are satisfying crop water needs. Soil moisture should be monitored where roots are most concentrated, usually in the plant row, and at two or three depth intervals. Changes in soil moisture are usually most noticeable near the soil surface (6 to 12 inches), where roots are concentrated. Under high water demand, soil moisture will be depleted at lower depths (2 to 3 feet below

the soil surface). Because fields rarely have uniform soil properties, soil moisture should be monitored at several locations. Methods that allow soil moisture to be tracked during the season are the most useful for irrigation scheduling.

Common methods of monitoring soil moisture include manually sampling with a soil probe and using the "feel method," and using instruments left *in situ* such as tensiometers, gypsum and granular matrix blocks, and capacitance soil moisture sensors. Many of the soil sensors can be interfaced with dataloggers that record readings at a predetermined interval. Data collected in these loggers can either be viewed in the field or downloaded to a computer.

Water Quality

Much of the coastal growing region for caneberries relies on groundwater, which can contain significant amounts of salts. Information on salinity effects on caneberries is limited. Published salinity thresholds for yield decline in blackberry and boysenberry are electrical conductivities (EC) of 1.0 dS/m for irrigation water and 1.5 dS/m for soil water extract. A 10 percent yield decline would be expected for an EC of 1.3 dS/m in the irrigation water and 2.0 dS/m in the soil extract solution. Blackberries have been found to exhibit toxicity symptoms when irrigated with water having boron levels greater than 0.5 ppm (mg/L). Varieties that tend to accumulate sodium or chloride in the canes may be more susceptible to yield decline than varieties that do not tend to accumulate these elements.

Chloride (Cl) readily moves in the transpiration stream and accumulates in leaves. Hence tissue analysis can be a useful tool for monitoring for toxicity symptoms. Toxicity injury will first occur on leaf margins and tips. Boysenberry and ollalieberry have been shown to tolerate up to 350 ppm chloride in soil water extract and 234 ppm chloride in irrigation water without exhibiting foliar injury. Raspberry is less tolerant to chloride than blackberries, showing foliar injury at 175 ppm chloride in soil water extract and 116 ppm chloride in irrigation water. Overhead irrigation can exacerbate foliar salt injuries and should be avoided if salinity levels are near the thresholds that would cause leaf injury.

Water with excessive levels of bicarbonates (greater than 6 meq/L) can lead to plugging of drip emitters, especially if calcium fertilizers are injected into the irrigation system, which can cause a calcium carbonate precipitate to form. Ammonia-based fertilizers, such as aqua-ammonia, can also cause bicarbonate precipitates to form by raising the pH of the irrigation water. Periodic treatment of the irrigation water with acids that lower the pH below 4 can minimize emitter plugging with carbonate precipitates.

Iron and manganese at concentrations greater than 0.2 mg/L (ppm) in irrigation water may potentially react with atmospheric oxygen to form iron oxide and manganese hydroxide precipitates in the drip system. Treatments such as aeration or addition of chlorine to the irrigation water can precipitate out iron and manganese before the water is used for irrigation. A settling basin, a sand separator, or a filter is required to remove precipitates upstream of the irrigation system.

As the crop adsorbs water, salts accumulate in the soil, especially in the root zone. Periodic leaching of the soil with water can prevent the buildup of salt to levels that may cause yield decline. Using winter rains for leaching salts can be an effective strategy in humid regions of the state. Drier regions must rely on irrigation water to leach salts below the root zone. Leaching is most effective in well-drained soils without any impeding layers. A general rule of thumb is that electrical conductivity of the soil water extract will closely approach the EC of the irrigation water using a 30 percent leaching fraction.

Soil Fertility and Nutrition

Soil fertility management is important for providing adequate nutrition for vigorous plant growth and for supporting the continuation of flowering and fruiting cycles. Large canes produce larger and more numerous fruit than small canes, while highest yields and quality come from plants with vigorous canes and leaves. A preplant soil test for phosphorus (P),

Table 6.3. Estimated water-holding capacity of soils with varying textures

Soil texture	Field capacity (~ 0.3 bar)	Wilting point (15 bars)	Available moisture
	Inches of water per foot of soil		
sand	1.2	0.5	0.7
loamy sand	1.9	0.8	1.1
sandy loam	2.5	1.1	1.4
loam	3.2	1.4	1.8
silt loam	3.6	1.8	1.8
sandy clay loam	3.5	2.2	1.3
sandy clay	3.4	1.8	1.6
clay loam	3.8	2.2	1.6
silty clay loam	4.3	2.4	1.9
silty clay	4.8	2.4	2.4
clay	4.8	2.6	2.2

potassium (K), calcium (Ca), and magnesium (Mg) can be used to indicate the fertilizer needs. Typically, soil nutrient levels of all of the macronutrients except nitrogen (N) and all of the minor elements should be maintained at optimum levels through preplant applications, and periodic application of nitrogen during the growing season provides nitrogen nutrition. Once optimum soil test levels are reached, repeating soil testing every third or fourth year is adequate.

The Olsen's Bicarbonate Extraction for phosphorus and the Ammonium Acetate Extraction procedure for potassium are most often used for neutral to alkaline soils in California because these methods give the most consistent relationship between soil phosphorus and potassium measured by these methods and crop response. Critical phosphorus and potassium levels have not been established for caneberries in California, but across a range of crops there is little or no plant response above 40 ppm phosphorus and above 200 ppm potassium. These levels can be used as the levels at or above which no fertilizer is required.

The routine nitrogen fertilizer applications should be made periodically during the growing season, from the time new canes emerge until harvest ends. Applications of nitrogen can be made weekly, biweekly, or monthly, as best suits the irrigation program and other management practices. First-year plantings and floricane-bearing varieties will require about 10 pounds of nitrogen per acre per month during the period from February until the end of harvest in the fall. Second-year and older primocane-bearing varieties in coastal areas with long fruiting seasons should receive 20 pounds of nitrogen per acre per month. Inexpensive, relatively soluble nitrogen fertilizers such as urea, calcium

nitrate, or ammonium nitrate can be broadcast on the soil surface and dissolved with overhead sprinkler irrigation (table 6.4). These materials may also be dissolved or applied as a liquid in furrow, sprinkler, or drip irrigation systems. However, sprinkler and furrow irrigation may be less efficient because they apply nutrients to inter-row areas and furrows. Drip irrigation allows the most efficient application of soluble nutrients.

Other solution fertilizers also exist, and special solutions can be prepared by fertilizer distributors.

Compost

Compost contains 1 to 2 percent of nitrogen, phosphorus, and potassium on a dry weight basis but often contains 25 to 28 percent moisture, so cost per unit nitrogen is increased by 25 to 33 percent. Compost must decompose before nitrogen is released. The nutrient value of compost alone probably does not justify its use, but it may be a useful source of organic matter and nutrients in very sandy soils.

Granular complete or simple single element or minor element fertilizers can be applied and incorporated in the bed to correct nutrient deficiencies of nutrients other than nitrogen. A uniform application should be incorporated in the bed as needed prior to planting. This is the best time to ensure a uniform fertilization. Subsequent applications of granular materials can also be made at any time as a banded application at the edge of the plant row, but the nutrients should be incorporated in the soil for best results. The solubility of fertilizer materials can vary considerably, and only water-soluble fertilizers can be applied as a liquid mixed with water. The water-soluble materials that are applied on the

Table 6.4. Characteristics of common nitrogen fertilizer materials

Fertilizer material	Nitrogen (%)	Form	Solubility in cold water (lb/100 gal)	Notes
ammonium nitrate	33.5	dry	984	—
ammonium sulfate	21.0	dry	592	—
monoammonium phosphate	11.0	dry	358	48% P
CAN 17	17.0	liquid	—	8.8% Ca
calcium nitrate	15.5	dry	851	—
urea	46.0	dry and liquid	651	—

Source: Adapted from Maynard and Hochmuth 1997.

soil surface will be readily available as they dissolve and move into the planting bed. Soluble complete fertilizers are also available; and although they are considerably more costly than granular fertilizers, they can be used to correct deficiencies by application in the irrigation water.

Growers desiring to produce caneberries organically can use a combination of preplant incorporated compost and annual surface application of compost. Compost is one of the more economical sources of other nutrients as well as nitrogen for organic growers, and compost also builds soil organic matter. Compost quality may vary from different supply sources. Broadcast annual compost applications are often supplemented by in-season application of higher analysis liquid organic fertilizers. These annual compost applications should be combined with application of liquid organic materials such as liquid fish waste or soy extract, to provide more readily available nitrogen during the growing season. These materials also must be in contact with moist soil for efficient utilization by the plant. Foliar minor element sprays or injection in the irrigation may be useful for correcting minor element deficiencies in organic or conventional fertilization programs.

Some foliar tissue testing is useful if nutrient deficiency is suspected, and it may also be used to help guide nitrogen fertilization. Foliar leaf values for major nutrients are summarized in table 6.5. To sample caneberry plants for a tissue analysis, collect 20 fully expanded whole leaves on new primocanes between May and August. Avoid sampling less than 18 inches from the tip of the cane. Sample each variety or each area separately. Ship the leaf sample in a paper bag to the laboratory via overnight mail. Mark each sample set with a number that will connect the sample to the field or variety.

Fertilizer Injection Devices

Caneberries and other small fruits respond to uniform moisture availability and intensive fertilization. Fertilizer injection allows growers to irrigate and apply fertilizer on a regular schedule and uniformly over the rows with less labor requirement and without danger of harming the roots or rhizomes. Irrigation systems are installed with a backflow prevention device to prevent backflow of fertilizers into the well or water source if the pump stops. Care must be taken to not overwater and leach soluble nutrients below the root zone.

Soluble dry fertilizers mixed with water or liquid fertilizers may be injected, as well as specially ground organic liquid fertilizer suspensions. Prior to injection, be certain the material is indicated by the manufacturer as appropriate for injecting in irrigation systems. The fertilizer should be injected above the filter system so that any material that could potentially cause plugging of drip lines is filtered out. The concentration of the fertilizer injection material is not critical but rather the total amount of nutrient applied to an area of land. For best results, run the irrigation system for at least 15 minutes before and after the injection process. The irrigation lines should also be flushed periodically to avoid plugging.

The two most commonly used injection devices are venturi-type injectors, which work on the different pressures created across a venturi, and positive displacement pumps powered by diesel or electricity. Another common type of device uses a pump powered by water pressure in the irrigation system. The venturi and water-powered pumps are commonly used injectors that are adequate for application of fertilizers. The positive displacement pumps are the most expensive, and the requirement for electricity or fuel to run the pump limits their use to larger installations.

Table 6.5. Normal range for raspberry foliar leaf tissue analyses

Macronutrient	Dry weight (%)	Micronutrient	Parts per million (ppm)
nitrogen	2.00–3.00	manganese	50–200
phosphorus	0.25–0.40	iron	50–200
potassium	1.50–2.50	copper	7–50
magnesium	0.30–0.90	boron	30–50
calcium	0.60–2.50	zinc	20–50

Source: Adapted from Pritts and Handley 1989.

7 Training and Pollination

Trellising

Trellising improves management of raspberries and blackberries grown for fresh market and optimizes production from small acreages. Trellising in general is used to support canes in an upright manner, especially needed by canes heavily laden with fruit. It is also used to improve air circulation and light interception and to minimize disease pressure. Flowering and fruit set is improved with better aeration and light distribution. Trellises also support heavy, fruit-laden canes to keep fruit off the ground and to facilitate spraying and picking operations. The newer primocane-bearing raspberries tend to be more erect as a group. However, they are also higher yielding and more productive than older cultivars, so the need for trellises persists with raspberries. Blackberry cultivars range from erect cultivars to semierect and trailing cultivars. Although the more erect cultivars are somewhat self-supporting, all of these blackberry types are easier to manage—and yield and quality are improved—with trellising.

Raspberry trellises typically attempt to train or contain plants within a hedgerow that is ideally 12 inches wide at the soil line and opens in a V shape vertically to approximately 3 feet wide at shoulder height. Different types of trellises can be used to obtain this configuration with raspberries. The simplest and most economical types use either a T-post configuration with two cross members at 3 and 5 feet high attached to wood or metal upright posts that are 4 to 5 inches in diameter and 7 to 8 feet tall, with 2 feet buried (fig. 7.1). No. 12 galvanized wire may be used on the upper pair of wires and pea string or line on the lower two lines. In systems where the primocane raspberry hedge is mowed to the ground each winter, it may be useful to use T posts and bury 2- to 3-foot sections of PVC to hold the posts for easy removal for mowing. Single end posts may also be used to train floricanes following pruning to a simple vertical, multiple-wire trellis (fig. 7.2).

Figure 7.1. Traditional T configuration for raspberry trellising, allowing development of V canopy for light and air penetration. *Photo:* Mark Gaskell.

Figure 7.2. Alternative trellising on three wires for floricane raspberry crop in tunnels. *Photo:* Mark Gaskell.

An alternative configuration uses two posts in an X arrangement, with two sets of double wires or twine to create the V shape at knee and shoulder height. The T or X posts are spaced every 20 to 25 feet, and end posts may need to be reinforced with cement or support wires, depending on the length of the hedgerow as well as the vigor and weight of the crop.

A common trellis system used by many tunneled raspberry growers in California involves a V trellis system with two pairs of cord lines and single posts spaced 20 feet apart down the row (fig. 7.3). Cord is wrapped around the posts at 3 or 4 spots between approximately 18 inches and 5 feet in height. That cord then wraps the other two pairs of lines on each side that restrain the plant canes. As the canes grow, they are inserted between the double lines of cord.

Blackberry plants are also best pruned and trained to a narrow row-wall configuration (fig. 7.4). Training to trellises improves the reception of light and can improve fruit yield and quality and decrease disease incidence. Blackberry trellises consist of two strands of wire, one at an 18-inch height and a second one at about 6 feet. More trailing or semi-trailing blackberries can be pruned at 5 to 6 feet in height. The lateral branches can be tied to the wires as needed to create a more or less solid wall of vegetation consisting of 4 to 6 primary canes from the base of the plant and the secondary lateral branches.

Figure 7.3. Alternative trellising for management of raspberry primocane crop in tunnels. *Photo:* Mark Gaskell.

Pruning

Raspberries

Pruning and training systems are specific to the plant type and the desired management effect. Traditionally, floricane-bearing raspberries and blackberries are pruned in the fall of the first season. The floricanes that grow in the spring of year two as secondary growth from these 1-year canes produce flowers and fruit in the summer of the second year. Following the production of the floricane fruit, the floricanes are pruned to the ground and the new primocanes are allowed to develop (fig. 7.5A).

More management options are available with the primocane-bearing type raspberries (fig. 7.5B). Primocanes, if left to flower and fruit, will produce on the tips of 1-year-old canes. Or if these canes are tip-pruned at 4 feet high or higher, the main cane will branch and multiple laterals from these first-year canes will flower and fruit in year one. This tipping practice stimulates greater production from varieties that are weak primocane types. It can also be used to postpone the production by 30 to 60 days in order to harvest during a more profitable market window.

Primocane-bearing types may be managed with a combination of cutback or mowdown pruning. In the cutback system, plants are pruned to 3 to 4 feet in height following the end of harvest, and the canes are manually stripped of leaves. This induces a mild dormancylike reaction in the plants. But following a brief rest, the canes sprout new branches and new canes emerge at the soil surface. Thinning can also be done at this time to keep canes to an optimum density of

Figure 7.4. Erect blackberries trained in a flat wall fan arrangement against two single wires as the trellis. Note that bottom wire supports drip irrigation tubing above soil surface. *Photo:* Mark Gaskell.

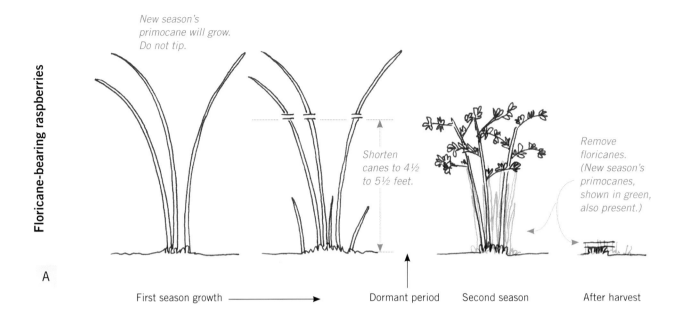

Floricane-bearing raspberries

New season's primocane will grow. Do not tip.

Shorten canes to 4½ to 5½ feet.

Remove floricanes. (New season's primocanes, shown in green, also present.)

A

First season growth ——————▶   Dormant period   Second season   After harvest

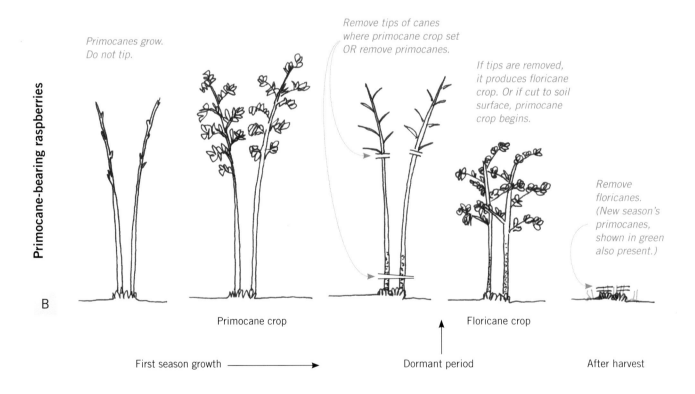

Primocane-bearing raspberries

Primocanes grow. Do not tip.

Remove tips of canes where primocane crop set OR remove primocanes.

If tips are removed, it produces floricane crop. Or if cut to soil surface, primocane crop begins.

Remove floricanes. (New season's primocanes, shown in green also present.)

B

Primocane crop   Floricane crop

First season growth ——————▶   Dormant period   After harvest

Figure 7.5. Pruning of (A) primocane-bearing and (B) floricane-bearing raspberries. Note that primocane-bearing raspberries flower on primocane tips for a primocane crop, or they may also be treated as floricane-bearing types for a second season harvest from floricanes. *Source:* Adapted from Bordelon 2001.

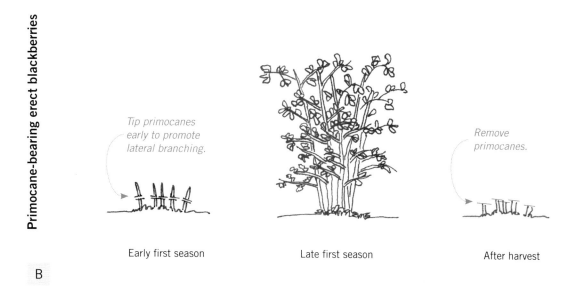

Floricane-bearing erect or semierect blackberries

Primocanes emerging, first season

Shorten canes to 4½ to 5½ feet.

Primocanes emerging, first season

Early first season

Late first season

Dormant period

Floricanes branching - new primocanes also starting (shown in green)

Floricanes bearing - new primocanes also present (shown in green)

Remove floricanes. (New primocanes, (shown in green, now in first season.)

A

Second season

Early second season

After harvest

Primocane-bearing erect blackberries

Tip primocanes early to promote lateral branching.

Remove primocanes.

Early first season

Late first season

After harvest

B

Figure 7.6. Pruning of (A) primocane-bearing and (B) floricane-bearing blackberries. Note that primocane-bearing blackberries flower on primocane tips for a primocane crop, and then they may be mowed completely to the ground for the following season. Early pruning of primocane-bearing blackberries facilitates manipulation of harvest period. *Source:* Adapted from Bordelon 2001.

four or five producing canes per foot of row. Flowering and fruiting occur on the lateral branches, and the cutback canes produce again in 3 months.

The mowdown of primocanes is an alternative pruning procedure where all of the canes are cut at the soil surface. This initiates a new round of primocane emergence, and flowering and fruiting commence on these canes in about 6 months depending on the temperature and growing conditions. Raspberries are harvested in 6 months following mowdown versus 3 months in the cutback, but yield is higher with mowdown. Normally, the mowdown is alternated with the cutback system to optimize the timing of fruit availability relative to the market. In some cases, the primocane types may be managed to only produce the primocane fruit, with canes pruned to the ground following production of the fruit at the tips of the primocanes. All canes can also be mowed to the ground in the winter dormant season each year and new primocanes allowed to grow in the spring.

The initial row should also be vigorously pruned back laterally to maintain a hedgerow width of no more than 12 inches by pruning to the soil surface. Research indicates that it may be possible to renew primocane-bearing plantings, as well as the vigor of the overall hedge in alternate seasons, by rototilling either side of an 8-inch hedgerow.

Blackberries

Blackberries also fruit on second-year wood, similar to floricane-bearing raspberries (fig. 7.6A). The vegetative canes of blackberries are trained on to the trellis in year one and are pruned (tipped) at 4 to 5 feet high, while the secondary branches are tipped again at 2 to 3 feet long. The branches are all trained to the wires.

In the winter of the first year, the bottoms of these primocanes can be sprayed with a band of white latex paint. In year two, flowers emerge from the lateral branches of the 1-year-old canes (now floricanes) and new primocanes are initiated at the base of the plant. Following the harvest in year two, the floricanes, marked with the white paint, can be cut back to the ground and the new canes left for the following year's fruit production. Those canes are then sprayed with a band of paint and so on.

New primocane-bearing blackberries offer the potential for more off-season production and protected production in high tunnels. The primocane-bearing types enable fruit production on primocanes and in the absence of chilling (fig. 7.6B). In some cases, low-chill-requiring blackberries such as Brazos, Roseborough, or Tupy have been successfully produced during off-season periods (primarily in subtropical conditions), but those alternative off-season cropping systems are not as well developed with blackberries as with raspberries. The new primocane-bearing blackberries offer the opportunity for off-season production and in low-chill conditions with superior fruit quality to these older low-chill varieties.

Pollination

Caneberry fruit quality and production is often improved by the use of honey bees or bumblebees for pollination. In small plantings bordered by native vegetation that lines riparian areas or other ample areas of diverse, perennial-flowering species, bees may not be necessary. If native bee populations are not adequate to provide vigorous numbers of pollinators, add additional hives. At least 1 or 2 hives per acre should be placed on field perimeters. For best results, move bees into the fields when flowering begins and keep them in place throughout the flowering season.

Part 3 Caneberry Harvest and Postharvest

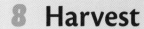

Caneberries are among the most perishable of fresh produce items, as they are extremely fragile and have a very short postharvest life. Caneberries must be harvested when they are nearly completely ripe in order to assure high eating quality, which increases their perishability. They have a naturally high metabolic rate, which also shortens their postharvest life, even in the absence of decay-causing organisms to which they are highly susceptible. Berry fruit have thin skins that are easily damaged by tears or bruising. In addition, the open cavity of raspberry fruit makes them especially susceptible to crushing and bruising damage. Physical damage further increases the metabolic rate of the fruit, increasing their rate of deterioration. Despite these challenges, raspberries and blackberries are successfully marketed during many months of the year and shipped to distant markets.

Success in handling these fruits requires particular attention to gentle handling and temperature management at every step after harvest. The amount of care taken will determine the quality of the fruit when it reaches the retail shelves and the consumer's home, and this will influence repeat purchases. Every handler—from harvest, storage, shipping, and marketing—can do damage to the berries that results in loss of quality, ultimately affecting the monetary returns to all handlers.

Importance of Temperature

The most important way to slow loss of quality and deterioration of berry fruit is to remove the field heat and maintain the fruit at a low temperature as quickly as possible. For maximum postharvest life and quality, fruit should be held as close to 0°C as is practical. Fruit respiration rate is closely related to the rate of deterioration. The respiration rate decreases 2- to 2.5-fold when fruit temperatures are reduced from 20° to 10°C, and it decreases 3- to 4-fold when fruit temperatures are reduced from 10°C to the optimal storage temperature of 0°C. In the field after harvest, berry temperatures can be as high as 30°C if fruit are left unshaded in the field.

Quality Control Procedures

To ensure successful marketing of caneberries, an effective quality control program should be implemented, beginning in the field and extending through postharvest handling and marketing. This should include field supervision of the harvest crew to ensure selection of high-quality fruit of the proper maturity, handling to avoid injuries, and avoidance of delays in cooling. The quality of the packed product should be evaluated on a routine basis and feedback given to harvest crews to allow for improvement. Records should be kept and routinely evaluated to determine where improvements can be made.

Grade Standards

U.S. No. 1 grade requires berries of one variety that are well colored (for raspberry, whole surface of a typical color of mature berry; for blackberry, whole surface is blue or black in color); well developed (not misshapened); not soft, overripe, or broken; and free from cores, sunscald, decay, or other damage (USDA 1931). Not more than 10 percent of a given lot can fail to meet this standard. U.S. No. 2 grade does not meet No. 1 standard but does not contain more than 10 percent by volume of seriously damaged berries by any cause and not more than 2 percent decay.

Harvest and Field Handling

Harvest Maturity

All berries should be harvested as near ripe as possible for the anticipated market, as eating quality does not improve after harvest. The decision on whether fruit is ready for harvest is generally based on berry surface color. Soluble solids and titratable acidity may also be considered. Raspberries should be harvested firm, ripe, and sound. The raspberries can be picked as soon as they can be slipped from the receptacle (fig. 8.1). The raspberry is fully ripe once it turns completely red, but sugars and acids may continue to increase as the color darkens and the fruit softens. Fruit sugar content continues to increase during fruit development on the plant, reaching 13 percent or higher—but it does not increase after harvest, although red color may continue to develop. Raspberries shipped to more distant markets will be picked at a lighter color stage, and berries picked for farm stand and local market sales may be allowed to darken and ripen further.

Blackberry fruit undergo distinct color changes during ripening, from green to red to black. The latter stages of ripeness occur rapidly in warm climates and are further defined as mottled (50 percent black), shiny black, and dull black. Generally, fully black fruit are harvested based on the ease of abscission from the pedicel. Harvest of immature berries can lead to a red discoloration developing after harvest. This defect is thought to be due to a lower pH and/or lower amounts of various pigments. Berries of many cultivars are not ripe when they turn black and should not be picked until they are sweet but still firm enough for marketing. This will vary among the cultivars and with weather conditions. For semierect and erect cultivars, only dull black blackberries should be harvested for fresh markets due to their higher sugar to acid ratio, while shiny black fruit may be acceptable for some cultivars. Fruit firmness at harvest influences blackberry shelf life, as soft fruit are more easily damaged during harvest and handling, and they are more

Figure 8.1. Raspberry being removed from the receptacle. *Photo:* Mark Bolda.

susceptible to pathogen infection. Fruit shipped to more distant markets are generally harvested at a firmer stage but typically will not be as sweet as if allowed to fully ripen on the plant. The higher sugar to acid ratio and sweetness are not due to a higher sugar content but lower acidity, resulting in a sweeter taste and better consumer acceptance. Acidity decreases by as much as 50 percent between the black and shiny black stages and 10 to 30 percent between the shiny black and dull black stages, depending on the variety. Acidity can also decrease by 10 to 30 percent in cold storage.

Harvest Methods

Raspberries and blackberries are harvested by hand. In large commercial plantings, the pickers harvest in small (1 quart) buckets held on their belt with a wire hanger, and later each picker packs the flats at a covered trailer placed near the harvesting rows. Then each picker is given piece-rate credit for the harvested flat, using a scanner and a button that the picker wears. The picker is paid at the end of the day via a computer program that automatically tabulates the payment. Each picker is assigned to specific rows to determine picking efficiency and quality for each picker separately.

Harvest should be as frequent as needed to avoid overmature fruit. The frequency will vary with the cultivar and temperature and may be as often as 1 or 2 times per week early in the season or 5 times per week at peak periods with warm temperatures. Typically 8 to 10 pickers are required per hectare (3 or 4 pickers per acre), increasing to 25 to 30 pickers at the harvest peak with mature plants. One picker can harvest 5 to 10 pounds of berries per hour, depending on the variety and the time of the season. Harvest in the cool morning hours, when berries are firm and easier to handle. Harvesting should stop each day when the weather gets warm.

The appropriate stage for harvest depends greatly on the cultivar, and some cultivars are more suited to long-distance shipping than others based on their storage characteristics. The force required to remove the fruit from the pedicel (blackberries) or receptacle (raspberries) varies greatly among cultivars. Fruit color should be within a fairly narrow range at harvest so that fruit will respond to postharvest handling in a similar manner. Pick all the ripe berries on the bush before proceeding to the next bush, and pick only well-ripened fruit. Immature fruit should be left for subsequent harvests. Overripe, diseased, or damaged fruit should not be left on the plant, as this will slow future flowering and fruit development.

Handle berries carefully. If fruit are injured during harvest, decay quickly sets in. Proper training of the picking crew is essential and should be followed by strict and detailed supervision to ensure picking instructions are followed. Use the thumb, index finger, and middle finger to pick the berries, using a turning motion rather than a pull. Avoid squeezing the berries by holding too many in the hand. Pick with hands together and palms up to catch falling berries, working from the outside of the plant in. Take care not to damage the fruiting spurs, as this will reduce both yield and grade. Fruit should be sorted carefully during the harvest operation to remove fruit with fungal lesions or other injuries. Transfer immediately and gently to the picking container; do not hold in the hand. Do not rehandle the fruit after transfer to the container. Separate very ripe fruit for other outlets at picking time. Two 1- to 2-liter containers can be fitted to a waist carrier, one for firm fruit suitable for shipping and one for fully ripe fruit for processing outlets. When the waist carrier is filled to the appropriate level, transfer to a hand carrier, which should always be kept in the shade. Avoid overfilling the containers.

Packaging

Fruit should be packaged as soon after harvest as possible so that it gets to the cooling facility within 1 hour of harvest. The packing stations should be protected from the sun to keep the fruit cooler. Packers must take care to avoid bruising the berries and should minimize handling of the fruit during the packing operation (fig. 9.1). Fruit should be sorted as much as possible when harvested to avoid additional handling and sorting during the packing operation. Packing materials should be protected from dust and soil. Shipping flats should never be set on the ground, as soil will contaminate the fruit below when the flats are later stacked. Fruit containers should be kept as clean and sanitary as possible at all times. This is important for decay control and food safety. Fruit are transferred gently into the clamshells, weighed, and placed in the cardboard tray. Avoid overfilling the clamshells, as this will cause compression bruising of many of the berries in the container.

A field inspection program designed to ensure that grade and product quality standards are being met can be a great asset. These inspections should include berry uniformity, level of ripeness, freedom from defects, presence of bruising, and, in some cases, soluble solids content. This inspection can also occur upon arrival at the cooling facility.

Keep packed containers in the shade at all times, and deliver fruit promptly to the cooling facility (preferably within 30 minutes of harvest). Dark-colored berries can quickly warm to temperatures above the air temperature due to the effects of solar radiation. Maintain roads between field and cooling facility to avoid rough surfaces and fruit damage.

California blackberries and raspberries are generally shipped in corrugated fiberboard trays holding 4 to 5 kilograms of fruit packaged in half-pint clamshells for the U.S. market or 4.4-ounce thermoformed plastic, vented clamshells with hinged lids (fig. 9.2). Trays are grouped together in a two-tray stack with wires at both ends protruding

Figure 9.1. Quality control in the field. *Photo:* Mark Bolda.

Figure 9.2. Box of 12 clamshells of raspberries, ready for market. *Photo:* Mark Bolda.

above the tray top and fitting into slots in the tray staked above. Three fiberboard tie sheets are placed on the sixth, tenth, and top tray layers. In this manner, the pallet is stabilized and therefore pallet straps and wraps are not needed. A previous study on tray and clamshell designs demonstrated that venting across the top of the tray and along the sides, aligned with the middle of the clamshells rather than between the clamshells, gave the most rapid forced-air cooling. Vent holes in the bottom of the flats had no effect on cooling rates. Flats cool best with vents aligned in front of the clamshells rather than between, providing more rapid and uniform cooling. Using smaller clamshells with less depth of product (no more than four berries deep) is important to prevent crushing of fruit at the lower levels in the container.

Temperature Management

Good temperature management, including rapid cooling after harvest and maintenance of low fruit flesh temperatures, is the single most important factor in minimizing berry fruit deterioration and maximizing fruit quality and postharvest life. Fruit should be transported to the cooler shortly after harvest and shifted directly into the cooler, without delays for inspection or other processing. It is recommended that cooling begin within 1 hour of harvest. Delays in cooling of red raspberry of up to 12 hours increased weight loss and decreased fruit firmness in proportion to the increase in delay (Robbins and Moore 1992). Red color continues to develop in raspberry fruit after harvest, as the red pigments (anthocyanins) continue to develop, and pH increases, causing the fruit to darken and become less red and more blue. This undesirable color change can be reduced by maintaining the fruit at low temperatures after harvest.

All caneberry fruit should be precooled in a forced-air cooler to remove field heat and cool the fruit to the storage temperature as soon as possible. Forced-air cooling is a specific method of cooling in which pallets are positioned around a fan so that cold air is pulled past the fruit within the package. A tunnel is formed by leaving space between two rows of pallets and covering the opening with a tarp except where the exhaust fan is located. Air is removed from the tunnel, creating a negative air pressure in the tunnel. Cold air flows through the trays and past the fruit into the low-pressure area (fig. 9.3).

Figure 9.3. Pallets ready to be brought into cooler for forced-air cooling. *Photo:* Mark Bolda.

"Seven-eighths cooling time" refers to the time required to cool the berries seven-eighths of the difference between their initial temperature and the cold air temperature. A 24°C berry in −1°C air is seven-eighths cool when it reaches 2°C. In this case, more than seven-eighths cooling time would be required to cool the fruit to a desired holding temperature closer to 0°C. To monitor the cooling of fruit in a forced-air system, the process should be based on the warmest fruit in the tunnel (table 9.1). This would usually be the fruit on the inside of the pallet farthest from the fan, but this should be verified with testing. Do not leave fruit in the forced-air cooler longer than necessary, as this will lead to excessive water loss. An accurate, calibrated probe thermometer must be used to determine fruit pulp temperatures. Accurate thermometers for the precooler air and storage rooms are also essential, and the room thermometer should be placed away from the door for the most accurate monitoring.

Cold Storage and Additional Treatments

Temperature and Relative Humidity

Once the fruit are thoroughly precooled, transfer the pallets to a cold room at 31° to 32°F and 90 to 95 percent relative humidity. It may be difficult to maintain fruit temperatures near 0°C if there is a lot of traffic in and out of the cold room. Minimize traffic or use an air curtain, and never bring warm fruit into the cold room. Berries are very susceptible to water loss, which results in shriveling and loss of gloss. The skin of raspberries and blackberries offers little protection against water loss. High relative humidity and lower temperatures in storage, as well as packaging in water vapor barriers such as plastics, can reduce this risk. Fruit should be marketed as soon as possible after harvest but should not be shipped or covered with pallet shrouds until they are thoroughly cooled. Blackberry and raspberry can be stored from 2 to 5 days. Fresh raspberries are not usually stored but marketed immediately. However, firm fruit may be held 1 or 2 days at 31° to 32°F with 90 to 95 percent relative humidity.

Decay Control Strategies

Botrytis cinerea (gray mold) and *Rhizopus cinerea* (Rhizopus rot) are the two main pathogens of berry fruit that cause decay. *Rhizopus cinerea* will not grow at temperatures lower than 5°C, and therefore temperature management is the simplest method of control. Gray mold can continue to grow at 0°C, but growth is very much slowed by low temperatures. The best way to control fungal decay in berry fruit is to cool quickly and maintain the fruit as close to 0°C as possible. Additional steps include preventing injury to the fruit to maintain the natural barrier to fungal decay, avoiding placement of decayed fruit into packages, and shipping under elevated carbon dioxide atmospheres, sometimes called modified-atmosphere transport.

Modified-atmosphere packaging for shipment with 12 to 15 percent CO_2 reduces the growth of *Botrytis cinerea* and other pathogens (such as *Rhizopus stolonifer*), and it reduces the respiration and softening rates of blueberries, raspberries, and blackberries, thereby extending postharvest life (fig. 9.4). The benefits are better realized when transport temperatures are 2°C or greater, because of the greater activity of the fungal pathogens. The greatest benefit would be expected in periods of cool, moist, or foggy weather, when free water might collect on the berries, increasing their susceptibility to *Botrytis cinerea,* or gray mold. Whole pallet covers, and sometimes consumer packages, are commonly used for containment of the modified atmosphere. Prompt cooling must be done

Table 9.1. Air flow characteristics and time needed to cool berries

Seven-eighths cooling time* for warmest fruit (hours)	Air flow (cfm/lb of berries)	Static air pressure across pallet (inches of water)
1.5	2.0	0.40
2.0	1.4	0.20
3.0	0.8	0.08
4.0	0.5	0.04

Note: *Seven-eighths cooling time is the time required to cool the berries seven-eighths of the difference between their initial temperature and the cold air temperature. A 24°C berry in −1°C air is seven-eighths cool when it reaches 2°C.

before fruit are placed in pallet shrouds or sealed, modified-atmosphere packages, because the packaging impedes further cooling. All preparation should occur in a refrigerated holding room, and pallet covers should be put on just before truck loading for transport. Care should be taken to avoid tearing the bag when the pallets are loaded onto the transport vehicle. There can be some off flavors as a result of high carbon dioxide treatment, depending on cultivar, temperature, and exposure time. These generally dissipate within a few days of removing the fruit from the pallet covers.

Transportation

The transportation period represents the major portion of the postharvest life of caneberry fruit. Temperature management during transit is critical. Thermostats should be set as close to 0°C as possible, depending on the accuracy of the thermostatic control equipment. Refrigerated loading docks are highly recommended for the extremely perishable caneberries. Use sealed loading doors that prevent introduction of warm outside air during truck loading and allow the berries to remain under refrigeration near the optimum temperature of 0°C. Keep the loading doors closed except when a truck is in place, and cool the truck before positioning for loading.

Because most fruit shipped by truck is shipped as part of a mixed load, successful transport depends on temperature management of other commodities loaded on the truck and the conditions encountered during the loading of these additional commodities. Any product to be loaded with caneberries should at least be capable of transport under high relative humidity (at least 90 percent)

Figure 9.4. Pallets in modified-atmosphere packaging. *Photo:* Mark Bolda.

and temperatures near 0°C. All products, including the caneberries, should be thoroughly cooled with pulp temperatures near 0°C before loading onto the truck—whether before, with, or after the caneberries. If other products are loaded without a refrigerated dock, the doors should be opened for the shortest time possible and the air-distribution system should be turned off only during the time the door is open.

The transport vehicle should be inspected to ensure that it is clean and operating properly. Doors should be well sealed and overhead air ducts in good condition. Whenever possible, request an air-ride suspension on every axle to minimize vibration damage to the fruit. Product should be loaded in the center of the trailer, away from the side walls, to prevent warming or freezing of the product from exposure to exterior temperatures. Dunnage blocks can be used along the sides and between the walls and the pallets. Care must be taken to avoid puncturing or tearing the bag when pallet shrouds with modified atmospheres are used.

If the transport distance by truck is too far, given the perishable nature of caneberry fruit, the product may be shipped by air. This is especially important for export markets. As for truck transport, the fruit must be thoroughly cooled to 0°C prior to installation of pallet shrouds, if used, and prior to loading into cargo containers. Fruit should be transported to the airport or freight forwarding facility in a refrigerated truck. Reflective pallet shrouds and specialized ice packs may be used to keep fruit temperatures low during air transport and handling on arrival. Regardless of possible breaks in the cold chain, it is always best to cool the fruit

and provide low temperatures whenever possible. Studies have shown that it is the duration of berry exposure to warm temperature that is related to product deterioration, with only limited influence from cooling and warming cycles. Although keeping the fruit constantly cold is best, any cooling is beneficial.

Handling at Distribution and Retail Centers

It is best to unload cold berries directly into the 0°C refrigerated warehouse. If the fruit are warmer than 2°C, they will benefit from being recooled before holding at 0°C. If reconditioning is needed because of the presence of decay, the fruit should be kept at 0°C and small lots removed for sorting.

Caneberries in pallet shrouds will warm a few degrees during the transit period due to their own heat of respiration and the lack of circulation of cold air within the pallet. For this reason, the pallet shroud should be removed upon arrival and the berries thoroughly recooled.

Recooling upon arrival can be accomplished by spreading trays of berries in a cold room when small volumes are involved. For a pallet or more, a small forced-air cooler can be constructed to pull cold air through the pallets of berries. Do not overcool the fruit, as this will result in excessive water loss.

Refrigerated holding time should be minimized because of the perishable nature of caneberry fruit. Fruit should be transported to retail markets in a refrigerated vehicle and placed in a refrigerated display case for retail sale.

Quality Changes

The color of red raspberry changes after harvest and during storage as anthocyanins develop and pH increases, causing the fruit to darken and become less red and more blue. This color change detracts from the appearance of the fruit and is affected by storage temperature. Color change is slower at lower temperatures.

Soluble solids content (SSC) increases in blackberry fruit as they ripen, especially between the 50 percent black and shiny black stage, and it increases during storage due to weight loss. There are greater changes in titratable acidity (TA) than in SSC as ripening progresses. TA decreases as much as 50 percent between black and shiny black stages and 10 to 30 percent between shiny black and dull black stages, depending on the cultivar. Following storage, TA decreases 10 to 30 percent, depending on the stage at harvest. Sometimes TA increases in very ripe fruit, again due to weight loss in storage. Blackberry fruit can develop a red discoloration after harvest. It is theorized that this is caused by the harvesting of less mature fruit, resulting in less total pigment and a lower pH or differences in the relative concentration of various pigments.

References

Ayers, R. S., and D. W. Westcot. 1985. Water quality for agriculture. FAO irrigation and drainage paper 29. Rome: Food and Agriculture Organization of the United Nations.

Bordelon, B. 2001. Raspberry fruit. HO-44-W. West Lafayette, IN: Purdue University Extension Service.

Bowling, B. L. 2000. The berry grower's companion. Portland, OR: Timber Press.

Crandall, P. C. 1994. Bramble production: The management and marketing of raspberries and blackberries. New York: Haworth Press.

Ellis, M. A., R. H. Converse, R. N. Williams, and B. Williamson. 1997. Raspberry and blackberry disease compendium. St. Paul, MN: APS Press.

Funt, R. C., M. A. Ellis, and C. Welty. 1997. Midwest small fruit pest management handbook. Bulletin 861. Columbus: Ohio State University, Bulletin 861. Ohio State University Extension website, http://ohioline.osu.edu/b861/index.html.

Galleta, G. J., and D. G. Himelrick, eds. 1990. Small fruit crop management. Englewood Cliffs, NJ: Prentice-Hall, Inc.

Hansen, B., L. Schwankl, S. Grattan, and A. Fulton. 1999. Scheduling irrigations: When and how much water to apply. Oakland: University of California Agriculture and Natural Resources Publication 3396.

Hansen, B., L. Schwankl, S. Grattan, and T. Prichard. 1997. Drip irrigation for row crops. Oakland: University of California Agriculture and Natural Resources Publication 3376.

——. 1998. Microirrigation of trees and vines. Oakland: University of California Agriculture and Natural Resources Publication 3378.

Maynard, D. N., and G. J. Hochmuth. 1997. Knott's handbook for vegetable growers. 4th ed. New York: Wiley.

Pollack, S., and A. Perez. 2006. Commodity highlight: Raspberries. Fruit and tree nuts outlook. USDA Economic Research Service website, http://www.ers.usda.gov/publications/fts/2006/07Jul/FTS323.pdf.

Pritts, M., and D. Handley. 1989. Bramble production guide. Ithaca, NY: Northeast Regional Agricultural Engineering Service-35.

Robbins, J., and P. P. Moore. 1992. Fruit quality of stored fresh red raspberries after a delay in cooling. HortTechnology 2(4): 468–470.

Snyder, R. L. 1994. Frost sensitivity and protection. In J. K. Hasey, R. S. Johnson, J. A. Grant, and W. O. Reil, eds., Kiwifruit: Growing and handling. Oakland: University of California Agriculture and Natural Resources Publication 3344. 61–67.

USDA Economic Research Service. 2006. Commodity highlight: Raspberries. Fruit and tree nuts outlook, July 26. FTS-323: 16–23.

USDA National Agricultural Statistics Service. 2010. Noncitrus fruits and nuts: 2009 summary. Washington, D.C. USDA Economics, Statistics, and Market Information System website, http://usda.mannlib.cornell.edu/usda/nass/NoncFruiNu/2010s/2010/NoncFruiNu-07-07-2010.txt.

Measurement Conversion Table

U.S. customary	Conversion factor for U.S. customary to metric	Conversion factor for metric to U.S. customary	Metric
inch (in)	2.54	0.394	centimeter (cm)
foot (ft)	0.3048	3.28	meter (m)
acre (ac)	0.4047	2.47	hectare (ha)
square inch (in^2)	6.45	0.15	square centimeter (cm^2)
square foot (ft^2)	0.0929	10.764	square meter (m^2)
ounce (oz)	28.35	0.035	gram (g)
quart, liquid (qt)	0.946	1.056	liter (l)
quart, dry (qt)	1.1	0.91	liter (l)
gallon per acre	9.36	0.106	liter per hectare (l/ha)
cubic foot per minute per pound (cfm/lb)	0.0010405	961.11	cubic meter per second per kilogram (m3·s-1·kg-1)
pound (lb)	0.454	2.205	kilogram (kg)
pound per acre (lb/ac)	1.12	0.89	kilogram per hectare (kg/ha)
pounds per square inch (psi)	6.89	0.145	kilopascal (kPa)
Fahrenheit (°F)	°C = (°F - 32) ÷ 1.8	°F = (°C × 1.8) + 32	Celsius (°C)

Index

Note: *Italic* type is used to indicate tables, for example, *47t*, and figures, for example, *7f.*

L

lacewings, 27
land preparation, 19–21
late leaf rust, 33
Latham raspberry
    immunity to RBDV, 36
    susceptibility to Phytophthora root rot, 29
Lauren raspberry, *9t*
layout of fields, 18–19, 21
leaching, of salts, 46
leaf diseases. *See* foliar diseases
leafhoppers, 27
leaf rollers, 25–27, *26f*
leaf spot, 30
leaf tissue analysis, 48, *48t*
light brown apple moth, 25–26
lime sulfur, 30, 33
loading for transport, 64–65
Loch Ness blackberry, 6, *13t*
loganberries, 8, *8f,* 30

M

Mac Black raspberry, 12
macro-tunnels
    areas best suited for, 18
    construction, 17
    ET values adjusted for, 42
    off-season blackberry production in, 54
    production cycles, 17–18
    raspberry trellis design, *49f,* 50, *50f*
    water savings, 40
    year-round production in, 18
magnesium
    foliar tissue levels, *48t*
    preplant soil test, 46–47
Malahat raspberry, *9t*
manganese, foliar tissue levels, *48t*
manganese precipitates, 46
maturity of fruit, 58–59, 66
Meeker raspberry, *9t*
minute pirate bugs, 27
mites
    eriophyid, 23–24
    as predators, 24
    redberry, 23–24, *23f*
    spider, two-spotted, 24–25, *24f*
miticides, 24
modified-atmosphere transport, 63–64, *64f*
monitoring soil moisture, 45
monoammonium phosphate, *47t*
mowdown pruning, 54
mowing, to control weeds, 37
mulching, 38
Munger raspberry, 12

N

natural enemies. *See* biological controls
Navajo blackberry, 6, *13t,* 34
new plantings
    irrigating, 39, 42
    nitrogen applications, 47
    weeding, 37
New Zealand varieties, 11
nitrate leaching, 40
nitrogen
    in compost, 47
    fertilizers, 47, *47t*
    foliar tissue levels, 48, *48t*
Nordic raspberry, 29
Nova raspberry
    characteristics, *9t*
    frost injury, 37
    resistance to late leaf rust, 33
nutrition. *See* fertilizers

O

oblique-banded leaf roller, 25–26
Obsidian blackberry, *13t*
off flavors, from carbon dioxide treatment, 64
oils
    for powdery mildew control, 31
    for redberry mite control, 23–24
    for spider mite control, 24
Ollalieberry, 6, *6f, 13t,* 46
Olsen's Bicarbonate Extraction, 47
orange rust, 33–34, *34f*
orange tortrix, 25–26, *26f*
Oregon production statistics, *1f*
organic fertilizers, 48
organic soil amendments, 20
Ouachita blackberry, *13t*

P

packaging of fruit
    in the field, 61–62
    modified-atmosphere packaging, 63–64, *64f*
pallets
    covers/shrouds on, 63–64, 65
    loading onto trucks, 64–65
    ready for precooling, *62f*
    stacking of, 62
Paraquat herbicide injury, 37
parasitic wasps, 27, 28
pests. *See* foliar diseases; fruit diseases; insect pests
phosphorus
    crop response to/critical levels, 47
    foliar tissue levels, *48t*
    preplant soil test, 46–47
Phytophthora root rot, 19, 29
Phytoseiulus persimilis, as spider mite control, 24
picking crews, management of, 59
pick-your-own farms, 8. *See also* direct–sale markets
plant characteristics, of main berries, 5–8